Published

a guide to
literature review,
outlining, experimenting,
visualization, writing, editing,
and peer review for your
first scientific journal article

Thomas Deetjen, PhD

Names: Deetjen, Thomas, author.
Title: Published: a guide to literature review, outlining, experimenting, visualization, writing, editing, and peer review for your first scientific journal article
Includes bibliographical references and notes.

ISBN: 978-1-734493-10-8

Book design by Thomas A. Deetjen

Contents

Introduction

Despair hollowed my gut as I read it: "…please revise your research article to address the reviewers' comments and resubmit." Two years prior I had left industry to pursue an engineering PhD. I wanted to shift my focus: to work on broader problems that would advance scientific understanding and make the world a better place to live. But the challenges of navigating my first research project were suffocating that noble ambition. The whole process had so many hurdles. I had spent months developing an unusable computer model, debugged my experiment multiple times, and battled two rounds of peer review. This latest email—an invitation to fight peer review round three—left me feeling desperate. Would I ever see this project published?

If research feels hard, it's because it is hard. For one, the work is outright difficult. To advance our project toward publication, we must complete a multitude of tasks. Some of those tasks are exciting. Some of them are tedious. All of them are hard work.

But the more challenging part of research is its mysterious process. We know that it begins with a research idea and ends with a published journal article, but the path between those points is unclear—especially to the novice researcher.

Yes, our first publication attempt is especially difficult. For one, we have no idea what we're doing. We've never completed the journey from research idea to publication, and that inexperience creates uncertainty. What task should we be working on? How do we know when that task is complete? After it is complete, what do we work on next? And how many subsequent tasks must we finish until our project is done?

Eventually, that uncertainty gives way to doubt. We compensate for that doubt by clinging to the tasks we feel most comfortable working on: if we doubt our writing skill, we may focus on experimentation. But we will eventually hit setbacks in our areas of competency, too. And when we fail at those tasks we feel the most skilled at, we begin to doubt whether we belong in a research environment at all.

Needless to say, these escalating doubts make it difficult to stay productive. When our work feels never-ending, when our best efforts fail our perfect standards, it's hard to muster the motivation to continue. It's also hard to ask for help.

And when we seek help, it's difficult to find adequate guidance. It turns out that our peers are just as clueless—and just as good at hiding it—as we are. And our supervisors, however generous, often lack the time to offer step-by-step assistance.

The result: novice researchers—despite our inexperience, insecurities, inefficiencies, and limited guidance—are expected to dive into the research process and emerge from the other end published. Amazingly enough, that actually does happen. I did eventually publish that first research project, and you might stumble your way to the end of yours. But the frustration, burnout, and anxiety nearly extinguished my fledgling research career. Sure, I learned from my failures, but did that first research project need to be so challenging? Was all that frustration really necessary?

My answer to that question is, "No." Truly, research *is* difficult work. But we can avoid many of the mistakes that push our first research project from difficult to demoralizing. A more productive work rhythm, a cohesive picture of the research process, and a step-by-step, task-oriented to-do list can help us avoid many missteps. And though I had to gather that information the hard way, I want to make it easier for you. That's why I wrote this book.

Goal of this Book

Before we get into the goal of this book, let's clarify the goal of our first research project. One goal might be to prove our worth. Although we might not admit it, we often see our first project as an opportunity to establish our researcher identity. But when our work defines our identity, we become defensive perfectionists who receive criticism as personal attacks and view imperfect research as a blemish on our record. Not only does that mindset produce anxiety, but our defensiveness keeps us from seeking help and our perfectionism keeps us from finishing our project.

Another goal for our first journal article might be to advance scientific understanding. That motivation is certainly noble, but for the novice researcher it's rather ambitious. It's rare for a single publication to substantially advance a research field. Knowledge develops slowly, and it takes a portfolio of research projects to push the boundaries of science. When we expect that impact from a single publication—especially from our first one—we're bound to be disappointed.

No, the main goal for our first project is much more modest. Its main goal is to give us an opportunity to learn how the research process works. Its main goal is to give us confidence.

And to achieve that goal, we don't need to produce a perfect, ground-breaking journal article. We need only a feasible research idea that yields an above-average publication.

Not the most exciting goal, perhaps, but once we have that above-average publication behind us, we can improve our research process and hold our subsequent articles to higher standards. And as some years go by, we may look back on a stack of high-quality publications and be proud of the contributions we've made to solving critical questions in our field. Or maybe we simply grasp the research process well enough to crank out a few good articles, shave some semesters off of grad school, and finish our dissertation in less time and with less stress. That sounds pretty good, too. In either case, we need to get this first publication out of the way.

> The goal for this book, then, is to guide the novice science and engineering researcher to publish their first journal article with as little frustration as possible so that they can gain the confidence to produce subsequent publications that will change the face of science.

Scope of this Book

The book pursues that goal by providing a step-by-step plan for advancing a project all the way from research idea to published journal article. It organizes the research process and breaks it into manageable tasks that steadily move us toward that goal. And it offers some productivity advice to help us complete those various research tasks more effectively.

Part One explores three productivity frameworks that help us become more effective researchers—the kind of researchers that can efficiently complete the mountains of work required to publish a scientific research project. These productivity frameworks teach us to motivate our research with questions, prioritize high-concentration work, and build consistency through habits. Part One concludes by helping us translate these abstract frameworks into concrete action items that will make our research efforts more effective.

Part Two—the bulk of the book—demystifies the research process. It divides the process into seven consecutive phases: Review the Literature, Outline the Project, Run the Experiment, Visualize the Findings, Write the First Draft, Edit into the Second Draft, and Revise until Published.

Each of these phases has its own chapter that explains the phase's goal, provides a series of step-by-step tasks to complete that goal, and instructs us when to move on to the next research phase. Each chapter ends with a recap of its main material including a flowchart that visualizes its main tasks.

If all goes well, you'll finish the book a more productive researcher who has successfully navigated the research process. In that process, you'll develop a research question, run an experiment to answer that question, write a manuscript to explain those answers, and maneuver that manuscript through peer review until it's published. And years from now when you're a distinguished researcher with scores of science-revolutionizing publications, you can write me a thank you note for helping you get this first journal article behind you.

Sound good? Then, let's get started.

PART ONE

Becoming a Productive Researcher

Becoming a Productive Researcher

This book empowers us to advance a research idea all the way to a published journal article. Primarily, that involves following a step-by-step process that organizes a heap of chaotic research tasks into an ordered plan of attack. That's all in Part Two of this book.

But we cannot begin our journey there. Publishing our first journal article is an extremely challenging project. It requires vision, organization, focus, consistency, and many other distinguished adjectives that describe a persona I'll call "the productive researcher."

This productive researcher manages their time to prioritize activities that produce consistent results toward achieving their research goals. They are the best version of our researcher selves—the ones that will be most successful in completing our research project.

For many of us, though, that persona feels a long way off. If there is a productive researcher inside us, we bury them under layers of doubt, insecurity, and procrastination. Our current motivations, priorities, and systems fall short of the productive researcher we hope to become.

I, at least, struggle through the research process. Some research tasks bore me: I can seldom muster the curiosity to read half of the literature that I ought to. Some research tasks irritate me: I bite my lip as I graciously reply to a journal reviewer's incomprehensible comment. Some research tasks spoil me; I can happily spend months ignoring reading and writing while I indulge interesting but unimportant side-experiments. These hurdles stifle my progress.

And even when I gather the right motivations, daily distractions keep me from completing the work. How often have I broken my focus to check my phone, chat with coworkers, or browse phdcomics.com for new content? How often have I let meetings, email, and extracurricular commitments steal time away from my research projects?

I tell myself it's okay because summer will come around. Summer will give me months of uninterrupted time to catch up. Except in summer I can't quite focus. My fast-paced semesters have trained my brain for sporadic activity instead of undistracted depth. My lack of focus yields unsteady progress, and I eventually realize that I'm not gaining ground as quickly as I had hoped. I take holidays here and there to deal with the resulting stress. But by the end of summer, I'm anxious, exhausted, hitting dead ends, and anticipating another fast-paced semester where catching up on research will only become more challenging. It's demoralizing!

These downward spirals can trap any of us, and they put our research projects in jeopardy. We enter these pits not because of research's difficulty, but because of our failure to cultivate our productive researcher. Our baseline persona—the poorly motivated, misdirected, unreliable part of us—might possibly finish our research project, but progress will move slowly with many more anxieties, missteps, and hurdles than necessary.

Fortunately, we can evolve. We can pursue an upward spiral that slowly liberates our inner productive researcher. We do this by defining our goals, prioritizing activities that advance those goals, and building systems that help us consistently accomplish those activities. Part One explains this process through the following chapters:

Motivate Research with Questions

First, we motivate our research with the correct goals. Aimless experimentation breeds perfectionism, individualism, and frustration. But a well-crafted research question places our work into the context of what other scientists have done before us and motivates our efforts toward an achievable endpoint.

Prioritize Deep Work

Second, we pursue that endpoint by prioritizing high-concentration activities. Many distractions can hinder the reading, experimenting, and writing tasks we must complete to advance our project. We need to prioritize those activities by making time for them, training our brain to concentrate on them, and resting our brain from them.

Building Consistency through Habits

Third, we consistently engage those high-concentration activities through habits. We often lack the willpower to make the decisions that lead to productive work sessions. But by developing better habits, we bypass our unreliable willpower and automate the behavior that supports our high-concentration activities.

Cultivate a Virtuous Cycle

Last, we synthesize these three philosophies into a unified productivity framework. We use seasonal planning sessions to translate that abstract productivity framework into a list of concrete action items. And we use weekly reviews to continually realign our behavior with that action items list.

1

Motivate Research with Questions

We have a noble ambition for our research—that it might advance science and improve society. Or more practically, that it might produce scientific publications that help fill our research field's most pressing knowledge gaps.

To embrace this ambition, our research must engage three activities. First, since research aims at knowledge gaps, we must study our fields' literature to know what those knowledge gaps are—we must read. Second, since research fills those gaps, we must produce novel data that reveal scientific truth—we must experiment. Third, since research communicates those new truths to a broader audience, we must publish our projects—we must write. Thus, reading, experimenting, and writing constitute research; to pursue our noble ambition, we require each of these skills.

I, for one, find that statement unnerving. My heart resonates with the ambition—research advances science and improves society. My mind understands the logic—to pursue that ambition requires reading, experimenting, and writing. But my actions exalt experimenting and downplay reading and writing. Why? Because I'm chasing the wrong motivation.

EXPERIMENT-MOTIVATED RESEARCH

Instead of pushing myself to fill a research gap, I naturally focus my efforts on mastering different experimental methods. Experimentation becomes my motivation. I feel that by pushing experimental boundaries I will eventually find some unexpected, novel result that alters science. I belittle reading because I trust too much in my own intuition. I downplay writing because I falsely expect groundbreaking science to reach an audience even if it is poorly written. I marginalize these soft, right-brained tasks to prioritize the systematic, left-brained experimentation.

Why do my motivations default to experimentation? For one, it's comfortable. I've always gravitated toward the objective, mathematic disciplines. Second, it's enjoyable. I can happily spend hours visualizing data, writing programming scripts, and developing computational models. Third, it's reinforced by my environment. My department emphasizes data analysis, scientific topics, and experimental methods over the softer skills.

These influences are far from nefarious—it's worthwhile to develop my technical competency. But when they motivate me to experiment for experiment's sake, my work becomes self-serving. My research no longer solves problems, it demonstrates my technical prowess. Experimentation gets tangled up in my own identity.

That identity crisis breeds perfectionism. First, imperfect experiments make me feel inadequate, so I pursue the highest level of quality to prove my value. Second, my lack of reading and writing rob my early work of a research gap and a publication plan. Without that guidance, I don't really know when my experimental findings are good enough to satisfy my research project; I have no criteria for success, so I default to producing work that is as perfect as possible.

Perfectionism is not an honorable devotion to high standards. It's a product of misplaced motivation, and it's a barrier to our success. It creates stress, fear, and doubt. We spend many hours pursuing an experimenting standard that we cannot meet. When we fail that standard, we lose confidence, and our work suffers, falling ever shorter of perfection.

Even if we avoid this downward spiral, our completed experimental findings will lack context. Near the end of our project, we must scramble through literature review and writing to fabricate a story that lends our experiment some broader scientific value. In the best case, we publish our project but feel whiplashed by the whole process. In the worst case, we find that our results don't actually fill a research gap, and we've wasted our time. It's all quite exhausting.

QUESTION-MOTIVATED RESEARCH

For the sake of our work—not to mention our own mental health—we need a better research outlook: one that connects us more strongly with our noble ambition, defines success by achieving specific outcomes, and reduces our need for perfectionism. To develop this new motivation, let's look beyond the research world and borrow some concepts from a classic book on productivity.

In his book, *The 7 Habits of Highly Effective People*, Stephen Covey gives some broad rules for how to work more effectively.[1] One concept urges us to "begin with the end in mind." Our actions should pursue a specific, predetermined goal. We don't undertake action for action's sake; we pursue action as a means to achieving our ends. Effective researchers, then, don't experiment for experiment's sake[2] but begin their research projects with an end in mind—publication.

Another concept encourages us to look beyond our individual projects and strive for interdependence. While an individualistic viewpoint praises autonomy, self-reliance, and diligence—all useful traits for the researcher—an interdependent viewpoint recognizes that we are even more effective when we contribute our strengths to larger projects; we can achieve more as a group than as individuals. We may idealize the independent researcher that secures their own funds, does their own experiments, writes their own articles, and reaps the awards. But effective researchers don't really operate in such isolation. They understand that they accomplish more as part of a research team. Or more broadly, they recognize that their work depends on the previous labors of other scientists. The interdependent researcher works within the context of the literature, pursuing problems that fill their field's research gaps.

Experiment-motivated research ignores these two concepts. It lacks a meaningful end for us to keep in mind. We may superficially work toward scientific understanding, but our most tangible goal is to perfect our experimental results. If we begin with that end in mind, we set ourselves up for failure. Experiment-motivated research also values individualism over interdependence. It is self-serving, asking how the research can validate us, rather than asking how the research can help our colleagues, research field, and humanity.

Question-motivated research, on the other hand, provides a stronger working paradigm. In question-motivated research, our work pursues a specific research question. We answer that question through experimentation. And we share our answer through a published journal article—an article whose findings advance science and improve society.

This question-motivated framework lets us work with an achievable end in mind—publishing a journal article that answers a specific research question. It puts us in a place of interdependence—relying on the literature to reveal worthwhile research gaps. This mindset elevates reading and writing, because those skills connect our work to broader science. Yet question-motivated research does not belittle experimentation. It streamlines experimentation by requiring results that may not be perfect, but are good enough to answer the research question. And it empowers experimentation by aligning it with a nobler cause defined by our research question: it replaces our experiment-motivated mindset with something much more effective.

CRAFTING A RESEARCH QUESTION

To change our mindset from experiment-motivated to question-motivated research, we must craft a strong research question. That research question guides our project. It's a north star that navigates us away from our individualistic pursuits and toward broader, nobler ambitions.

A research question yields practical benefits as well. It filters our time: it helps us prioritize seminars, reading, and meetings that contribute to our research question's solution. It gives us a talking point: it helps us answer "what are you working on" with our succinct research question instead of a bumbling description of our experiment. And as we'll see later in the book, a well-crafted research question eases the writing, editing, and revision process.

The research question interacts with two other mechanisms—the research gap and the hypothesis. The research gap describes a void in scientific understanding. It tells us what is unknown. We find it by identifying unanswered questions in our field's literature. The hypothesis describes our best guess at what the research gap will reveal. It uses our imagination to heighten our interest in the research gap. The research question sits between the gap and hypothesis: it identifies the specific part of the research gap that we aim to discover and provides a framework for the hypothesis to work in.

How do we design a research question that accomplishes all this? Though the components of a well-crafted research question vary slightly by discipline, we can all benefit from following a few common guidelines. A good research question harnesses our curiosity, creates social and scientific value, seeks broad application, and respects our unique research limitations.[3]

To illustrate these guidelines, suppose we have a friend pursuing her PhD at a well-regarded wizardry university where she specializes in the field of potions-making. Let's apply these research guidelines to her unique situation.

Harness Curiosity

We need a research question that strongly interests us. Research is hard work. When our noble ambitions fail to drive us, our fascination may carry us through a difficult slog. Even when funding sources constrain a project's research scope, we can still tailor it slightly toward our interests. We can identify research areas that engage us, find curious research gaps, and build exciting hypotheses. Then we connect our research gap and hypotheses with an intriguing research question.

Our potions-making friend concentrates on the sub-field of fur-infusion, which designs potions using a solvent, enchantment, and animal hair. These fur-infused potions temporarily endow the potion-consumer with some characteristic of the hair-donating animal. It's a bit weird, she admits, but ever since she brewed her first canine-honey mixture using golden retriever hair and experienced the insatiable desire to follow her mother around the house all day, she's been fascinated. Given her fascination, she supposes that any research question exploring fur-infusion will maintain her curiosity.

Create Value

To create value, our research question must have potential for both social benefit and scientific novelty—i.e., it may improve society and fill a research gap.[4] Projects without scientific novelty may benefit society, but they fail to advance scientific understanding and are therefore unpublishable. On the other hand, scientifically-novel projects that lack clear social benefit are risky. True, some such studies eventually realize enormous value. But the majority do not. Just because a research gap exists does not mean it needs to be filled.

From a potions-making perspective, there is, of course, little value in the heightened social neediness endowed by golden-retriever fur-infusions. Our friend must expand her interests toward topics that promise more useful social benefits and that advance potions-making understanding.

One of her ideas explores a potion that makes wizards more industrious. The literature already discusses the social benefit of such a potion. In fact, many potion-makers have attempted fur-infusions using the hair of highly-productive animals—beavers, for example—but with little success.

Rather than add to these unsuccessful attempts, our friend considers the developing field of trait-reversal. Instead of using trait-reinforcing solvents like honey, trait-reversal theorizes that some solvents might endow potion-consumers with the opposite traits of the hair-donating animal. Although trait-reversal is a nascent potions field, our friend knows of one successful potion that temporarily suppresses hunger using a vinegar-pig-hair infusion—though the potion's flavor, admittedly, might confound the findings. Still, a project that explores trait-reversal fur-infusions for improving wizard productivity has potential social and scientific value, and our friend is interested in exploring it.

Seek Breadth

We can maximize our project's impact by crafting research questions that have broad scientific application. When we confine our research question within our own field, we limit its potential impact. But if we consider how a knowledge gap extends beyond our niche area, we can frame our research question to encompass additional scientific disciplines.[5]

Our friend's current scope—trait-reversal fur-infusions for improving wizard productivity—is, frankly, too narrow. If her project succeeds, she must consider how it might advance the broader potions-making field. Obviously, it will advance the niche topic of trait-reversal fur-infusions. But if she can connect her work to trait-reversal studies beyond the fur-infusions niche, she might contribute to a general theory of trait-reversal that spans multiple potions-making disciplines.

Respect Limitations

Although we prefer broad, valuable, interesting projects, we must avoid complex research questions that we cannot confidently answer. We must balance our research question with practicality. In particular, novice researchers with limited resources must carefully judge their limitations. They must assess their mentorship, support, and laboratory access before pursuing too broad of a research question.

Our potions-making friend faces two primary limitations. First, given her limited procurement budget, she decides to focus on indigenous animals whose hairs have successfully produced laziness-inducing fur-infusions. (By trait-reversing a laziness-inducing potion, she might successfully create a productivity potion.) Luckily, she knows of an experiment where cat-hair infusions, meant to make gullible people more wary, instead gave participants the desire to lounge around the house all day. Second, to test potions using clinical trials on actual wizard subjects requires significant regulatory oversight. To avoid that bureaucracy, our friend decides to test her potions on a non-wizard species. Since it would be futile to test productivity-potions on the already-industrious dwarves, she settles on a lazier species—garden gnomes.

Though she will develop her research question further during the literature review phase, our friend has a general direction for her project. She will use hair from a laziness-inducing potion—perhaps cat hair—to attempt a trait-reversal fur-infusion that produces industriousness in garden gnomes. It's an intriguing question that she has the resources to answer, and its successful outcome may both improve wizards' lives and contribute to a broader theory of trait-reversal potions design.

A well-crafted research question starts our project on a successful path. It underpins question-motivated research—a paradigm that pursues interdependence and begins our project with an achievable end in mind. It elevates our reading and writing without diminishing the value of experimentation. And it aligns our work with novel scientific pursuits that stand to benefit humanity. These all contribute to a shift in our mindset—a shift that begins to liberate our inner productive researcher. To continue this liberation, though, we need more than just a new motivation: we need to chase that motivation by prioritizing the activities that will help us steadily pursue it.

2

Prioritize Deep Work

In the previous chapter, we began to liberate our inner productive researcher by adjusting our motivations: we decided to pursue broader, nobler ambitions by motivating our research with questions. Pointing our work in the right direction is a vital first step. But we cannot advance in that direction until we align our actions with those motivations—until we rethink our priorities.

To prioritize our actions, we must first acknowledge a fundamental human limitation: our ambitions exceed our resources. We lack the energy to accomplish every goal. We lack the time to commit to every opportunity. Whenever we say "yes" to one thing, we must say "no" to many others. That means we must decline some goals and opportunities so that we can effectively accomplish others. That tradeoff is the essence of prioritization.

When I fail to prioritize important tasks, they are inevitably displaced by lesser commitments—because I hate telling people "no." Saying "no" feels like letting someone down, failing an obligation, or neglecting an opportunity. So I'm inclined to accept requests for feedback, offers to help on a project, or opportunities to coordinate some program. But if I'm not careful, I say "yes" too many times. The outcome: my schedule becomes so full, my email so overflowing, and my to-do list so long, that I end up doing everything poorly, especially my research. It's not that I'm spending my time on frivolous pursuits. The problem is that I haven't truly prioritized my noble research ambitions or the activities that will help me accomplish them.

MISPLACED PRIORITIES

My junior year of undergrad was the last time I said yes to everything. During that fall semester, I took seventeen hours of course credit, had a girlfriend, and directed the planning of a leadership conference along with other commitments. I had successfully juggled all my obligations up to that point. But that year I got my first C. And my second, and my third. I felt miserably overworked and hopelessly out of control. I simply didn't have enough time in the day to get everything done. My coursework, which should have been my highest priority, got pushed to the fringes of my schedule.

Grad school made overcommitment even riskier. The coursework became more demanding, the extracurricular opportunities increased, and looming over all was the knowledge that I should be advancing my dissertation. An overfull schedule didn't just risk lower grades, it threatened slower research progress, which would yield extra years of being stressed out, underpaid, and uncredentialed.[6]

When I overcommit myself, I have to cut back somewhere. I tend to prioritize the fixed appointments in my schedule and my commitments to other people. This means that meetings, classes, seminars, and email management creep to the forefront of my schedule. My leftover time goes to research.

When I verbalize that, though, it sounds quite backward. Research should be my priority. But I schedule it like it's the least important thing on my to-do list. I've misplaced my priorities and have tailored my schedule around less important tasks.

Why? Partly because I view research as inherently flexible. I think that I can successfully read, experiment, and write at will. And because I think that, I have a hard time defending any scheduled research time from intrusions. Moreover, because I assume that my peers view research with the same flexibility as I do, I feel awkward excusing myself to prioritize it.

But that viewpoint is wrong. The tasks that advance our research ambitions—reading, experimenting, and writing—require significant concentration. We cannot successfully complete those tasks until we make them a priority. That means giving them a prominent position in our schedules, defending them from interruptions, and improving our ability to concentrate. We can accomplish all three by adopting a philosophy of "deep work."

THE DEEP WORK PHILOSOPHY

What exactly is deep work? Cal Newport describes it in his book—with the appropriate title, *Deep Work*—as work that requires our full cognitive capacity.[7] We accomplish it only in a state of distraction-free concentration. Deep work enables us to quickly master new skills and to perform them at elite levels. It involves creative, challenging tasks that are difficult for others to replicate or for computers to automate. Its outputs are meaningful, valuable, and lasting.

In contrast, "shallow work" is easily replicated by others or automated by a computer. It's simple, logistical, and can often be done while distracted. Its outputs are useful but fleeting.

Shallow work is not inherently bad. Email, meetings, and administrative tasks keep our world moving. The problem is that shallow work tends to push deep work from our schedule: shallow work is much easier to accomplish than deep work, and it feels more rewarding because we see its results immediately. But deep work—not shallow work—is what advances our research direction. Thus, part one of the deep work philosophy involves pushing shallow work to our schedule's fringes so that deep work retains priority.

Deep work, however, is more than manipulating our schedules to prioritize challenging tasks. It's also the cognitive ability to sustain intense concentration. We cannot finish creative, challenging tasks without that mental capability.

Unfortunately, many of us practice deep work so rarely that we cannot sustain prolonged concentration. The brain we need for deep work is, inconveniently, the brain we also use for leisure. When our brain gives us the least sign of boredom, we appease it with some entertainment, and that entertainment is often of a fast-paced, multi-tasking quality. Can we remember the last time we were bored and we purposefully avoided our phone? We cannot expect the brain which is immediately rescued from boredom during our downtime to somehow overcome monotonous reading, difficult experimental setups, or writer's block with focused determination.

Our frequent task switching, social media breaks, and fast-paced entertainment have not conditioned our brain for deep work, but for something more sporadic. Thus, part two of the deep work philosophy involves training our brain to achieve greater concentration.

Even with intentional training, our brain's ability to sustain intense concentration is limited. Deep work saps our brain's energy. We cannot spend unlimited time there; Newport's book suggests four hours of deep work as a typical daily threshold. Once our brain exceeds that threshold, our productivity plummets. If that's true, then we complete the greatest amount of deep work by focusing deeply for a few hours each day—not less, not more.

Luckily, when we aren't using our brain for deep work, it subconsciously works on our problems. We've all experienced times when we've felt particularly stuck on a task—where no amount of deep work can solve it. But when we finally give up and switch to other efforts, our brain will eventually, perhaps days later—usually when we're exercising without access to paper and pen—serendipitously find a solution. Thus, since our deep work capacity is limited, and our brain needs subconscious working hours, part three of the deep work philosophy involves pursuing daily rest.

DEEP RESEARCH EXAMPLES

Based on our discussion so far, the productive researcher pursues broad, noble research ambitions by motivating their research with questions. They steadily answer those questions by accomplishing deep research tasks—i.e., high-concentration tasks that are vital to completing a research project, such as reading, experimenting, and writing. The productive researcher accomplishes these high-concentration research tasks by pursuing a deep work philosophy—a philosophy where they devote time for deep work in their schedules, train their brain for prolonged concentration, and rest themselves each day.

If that sounds vague, let's make the deep work philosophy a bit more concrete by discussing a few examples. The following ideas show how I've applied deep work concepts to my own research routine. These examples are neither comprehensive nor required. Think of them rather as illustrations meant to stimulate your own ideas for pursuing deep research.[8]

Make Time for Deep Research

The first place we prioritize deep research is in our schedule. By intentionally allocating time for both deep and shallow work, we accommodate our deep research needs and reduce shallow work intrusions.

For example, I start each day with a few minutes of planning: I decide which deep tasks to prioritize and I schedule time to work on them. I do that by building a half-hourly schedule of my day.[9] First, I fill in immovable time commitments like meetings, course lectures, and appointments. Next, I block out a few hours of deep work time. Then, I assign a task to each of those deep work sessions. I can spontaneously adjust the schedule if needed, but I find that simply planning the day in advance helps me pursue reading, experimenting, and writing with greater intention.

To avoid neglecting shallow work,[10] I give it a recurring spot in my daily schedule—usually in the afternoon when my tired mind has exhausted its deep work potential. Most semesters, I can find a 90-minute timeslot during which I'm available every weekday.[11] Let's say, for example, that I'm free Monday through Friday from 1:30 to 3:00—I make that my shallow work timeslot. I use that time to check email, complete busy work, and schedule meetings. But I also use it to protect my deep work sessions from interruption: if someone wants my attention before 1:30, I simply tell them, "I'm busy now, but you can stop by my office any day between 1:30 and 3:00."

Train for Deep Research

To train our brain for deep research, we must both improve its ability to concentrate and reduce its tendency to distraction. In other words, we need to solve more mentally-strenuous problems and consume less sporadic, fast-paced entertainment.

I challenge my brain's concentration by clocking my writing productivity. When I write, I work in fifty-minute segments. At the end of each segment, I record the number of words that I've written. By regularly logging these results, I can compare my writing efficiency over time and see whether it's improving.[12] Frequently, I challenge myself to write a specific number of words—usually 120% of my average. My brain gains focus by working hard to meet that competitive goal.

I avoid sporadic, multi-tasking activity—frequent social media glances, in particular—by limiting my smartphone use. At work, I disable it—I active "Do not Disturb" mode, in which only a handful of people can call me—and put my phone out of sight. At home, I constrain my smartphone use: I wait until after dinner and then check it as much as I want until an hour before bedtime.[13] These restrictions prevent worktime distractions and reduce my brain's exposure to fast-paced screen time.

Rest from Deep Research

To recharge our brain's deep research capacity, we must give it daily rest. It will reward us with fresh mental capacity tomorrow and, in the meantime, by subconsciously pondering our unsolved questions.

The best way I've found to achieve consistent rest: give each workday an end.[14] Every day at 5:00pm, I begin a shutdown routine. I allot 15 minutes to reach a stopping point in my current task. I record any unfinished tasks—I will reevaluate them during next morning's planning session. Then, I shut down my laptop and end my workday. That's tough to do in an academic setting where many peers seem to work all evening, but I'm convinced of my evening downtime's value.

I use some of my non-working time to maintain my health. I know first-hand that poor nutrition, inconsistent sleep, and limited physical activity eventually torment my body. Headaches, drowsiness, an aching back, and other maladies, however minor, really sap my effectiveness. But my free evenings give me time to cook a healthy dinner, go on a walk, and get to bed at a reasonable hour. My past physical ailments remind me of those activities' importance.

Devoting time for deep work in our schedules, training our brain for prolonged concentration, and resting ourselves each day all help us pursue deep research activities. Deep work is essential to the reading, experimenting, and writing we must accomplish to answer our research question. As we engage deep work more often, our productive researcher persona gains a steadier foothold. But to fully unleash it, we must engage deep work more consistently by building better habits.

3

Build Consistency through Habits

The previous chapters introduced two strategies to help us strengthen our inner productive researcher. First, to better pursue our noble ambition of improving science and society, we orient our work toward solving research questions. Second, to better align our actions with that motivation, we prioritize deep work. But we will struggle to implement these strategies with any consistency until we develop day-to-day tactics for pursuing them. To build this consistency, we must develop our habits.

The weakness in those two productivity strategies—and the weakness with all strategic planning for that matter—is their unclear, short-term application. Yes, we need better motivations and better priorities. But with that strategic planning behind us, we must now sit down and do the actual work. We must pursue that strategic vision with consistency. But how?

My old answer to that question: I will pursue that strategic vision through willpower. But willpower has proven an unreliable ally. Maybe burnout has cooled my inner fire. Maybe cynicism has dampened my motivations. Or maybe I'm just tired. But as I begin each new day—with my noble motivations, with my deep work priorities, with my computer cursor blinking at me—I must first challenge two chronic lies—two lies that willpower often lacks the strength to conquer.

UNRELIABLE WILLPOWER

The first lie that I face anew each day: my project is so large and the deadline so far that delaying for one day won't cause any harm. This is the dark side of beginning with the end in mind. Sometimes the end is so distant, that I feel no loss in delaying its start until tomorrow.

The second lie: I lack the focus to do this. As I sit down to attempt some deep work, there are so many small tasks percolating through my brain. They all seem important—I should respond to that email from my supervisor, I really ought to see if anyone liked my social media post, I feel compelled to finally decide if my new Dungeons and Dragons character is a gnomish sorcerer or a half-orc bard.

These lies give a foothold for my inner procrastinator to overtake my dwindling willpower. I've scheduled this time for deep work; I should push those shallow tasks until later, but I'd really rather do them now and I'm not sure I have the willpower to resist them today because my dog howled at the moon three times last night and my coffee isn't quite brewed how I like it and shouldn't I just clear my head by completing a few small tasks so I can build up the confidence to work deeply a bit later?

Like all seductive lies, the danger with these two is their reasonableness—because they're partly true. It's true that we can easily recover a lost workday over the course of a year. It's true that we struggle to favor deep work over distraction. And because these lies are partly true, we cannot fight them with some logical, internal debate. We need a more foolproof tool, something that can insulate us from our frequent short-term lapses in willpower. We need habits.

HARNESSING HABITS

Planning, motivations, and good intentions only engage the far-sighted, conscious part of our brain; they align our strategic decisions with a particular direction. But at 9:58am—when we're plugging away at writing our book and our mind snaps to a realization that "plugging away" is really a strange phrase and we should consider looking up the etymology—we lose any notion of the goals we are trying to accomplish next year. There is only us, our brain, and the sixty seconds until 9:59am.

In those sixty seconds, we are saved or defeated by our subconscious. Our subconscious constantly works behind our active thoughts. Though its background activity can cripple us with distraction, we can also harness it to strengthen our daily work rhythm. We can align that subconscious activity with our conscious strategic decisions. We can trick our brain to shun unproductive distractions and crave the tasks that advance our research project. To do so, we must consciously manipulate our habits.

In his book, *Atomic Habits*,[15] James Clear shows how we can harness our subconscious and transform our daily routines by manipulating the chain of events that undergird our habits. Habits progress through a series of subconscious events: cue, craving, response, and reward. Cues are events that trigger a craving. Cravings are desires to acknowledge that cue with a response. Responses perform some action that secures a reward. And rewards condition the habit; a desirable reward reinforces the habit chain but an undesirable reward weakens it. The more we complete a chain with a desirable reward, the more that chain is reinforced until it becomes ingrained as a fully-fledged, subconscious habit.

The power of habits is easily understated. Subconscious habits boast many benefits over conscious activity. They require less thought energy, are automatic, and are more consistent. When our rhythms are filled with bad habits, we use a lot of energy to fight against them in our chaotic, daily struggle to get things done. When our rhythms are filled with good habits, though, we traverse our work tasks automatically and save our energy for creativity, critical thinking, and other deep work.

By demystifying habits as a cue-craving-response-reward chain, we empower ourselves to consciously manipulate that chain. As a result, we can connect our question-motivated, deep-work-prioritizing strategy with the subconscious rhythms that drive our daily activity. No willpower needed; we can simply refine our habits to indulge daily tasks that consistently march us toward our goals.

Though habits are a powerful subconscious tool, they do have their weaknesses. For one, building useful habits requires strategic awareness. We must design our habits to support our long-term goals. We may hear of an impressive habit idea—read a journal article every day, exercise every morning, brush our teeth each night before bed. But no habit is inherently good. If a habit clashes with our goals, we can ignore it. Only habits that integrate with our broad productivity strategy will support us in achieving our aims.

Habits also develop quite slowly. They require a lot of repetition to go from new to ingrained. Moreover, the complex habits that really empower our deep work rhythm are built on multiple integrated habit chains that can each take months to routinize. Habit manipulation is not an overnight fix to our productivity problems. It's part of a slow metamorphosis.

Finally, habits function subconsciously on short timescales: they don't help us achieve difficult, conscious activities. A good habit is merely a gateway. It is a mindless ritual that points us toward an actionable direction.[16] We cannot, for example, automate reading comprehension, experimental analysis, writing, or the other high-concentration tasks that constitute the research process. But we can automate the chain of events that lead us to sit at our desk each morning with a fresh cup of coffee, an open laptop, and limited distractions.

HABIT MANIPULATION EXAMPLES

Given that background, let's discuss a more practical question: how do we actually build better habits? To adjust a habit, we must consciously manipulate its cue-craving-response-reward chain. That is, to create good habits we emphasize the cues, strengthen the cravings, ease the response, and savor the reward.[17] To break bad habits, we use the opposite tact.

To clarify that strategy, I'll describe a couple of ways that I've recently manipulated my own habits. In the first example, I built a habit of waking up early to enjoy some alone-time and jumpstart my workday. In the second example, I quit a habit of breaking my work concentration to consume entertainment. I'm not necessarily suggesting you adopt these particular habits, though they work well for me. Consider them rather as examples of how to analyze and modify a habit chain. Then, apply that strategy to develop habits that align with your unique productivity goals.[18]

Emphasize the Cue

We emphasize cues by making them obvious. That can be as easy as identifying the cues: we often simply fail to notice the triggers behind our habits. Once we identify those triggering events, we can modify our environment to highlight them.

In my case, the cue is waking up. More specifically—since I often wake up more than once during the night—the cue is waking up between 6:00 and 7:00am. To highlight that event, I bought an illuminating alarm clock, which I set to shine at 6:00am. If I wake up to a dark room, I roll over and go back to sleep. If I wake up and the clock is lit, I have my cue.

Strengthen the Craving

The anticipation of a reward can entice us even more than the reward itself. To build strong cravings, then, we must tempt ourselves with alluring rewards. That means our habits must end with an attractive prize, and we must define that prize beforehand so that we can crave it.

The real rewards of early rising are solitude and a jumpstart on work—but it's difficult to roll out of bed craving such abstract desires. So I tempt myself with a more material prize: coffee. I started buying better coffee beans and setting my coffee maker to automatically brew at 6:00am. Now I wake up, smell coffee, and sense that my reward is close at hand.

Ease the Response

Even with obvious cues and strong cravings, many barriers can stifle our response. To continue the habit chain, we must remove those barriers and replace them with systems that encourage us to respond affirmatively.

Before the sun rises, I can find many reasons to stay in my bed. But my biggest barriers to early rising are tiredness and cold. To fight tiredness, I need seven hours of sleep: I need to be in bed by 11:00pm. To fight cold, I put my sweatpants within reach, so I can bundle up before leaving the covers. These two systems greatly improve my prospects of getting out of bed to indulge my coffee craving.

Savor the Reward

To reinforce a habit, the reward must be immediate; we must quickly reward our response with the craved prize. When we fail to reward the response, our brain questions the habit's value, and we lose some habit-building momentum.

As soon as I enter the kitchen, I set laptop and books on the table, pour a cup of coffee, and sit down. Then I cradle my mug in hand and relish the steamy, dark elixir. As I savor my prize and anticipate my morning solitude, I feel convinced of this habit's virtue.

That straightforward, early-riser example illustrates the basics of habit manipulation. But we can use those concepts to solve more complicated challenges. Consider the following example of shifting a bad habit toward a productive alternative.

For years, I struggled with losing concentration to entertainment—playing video games, checking social media, making sure those falsified sentences I put into Wikipedia still exist. And after some unproductive amusement, I'd shame myself back into work, only to slip back minutes later into more diversions.

To break that discouraging habit, I had to understand its cue-craving-response-reward chain so that I could manipulate it. Here's what I came up with:

> Cue: I repeatedly failed a task—unsuccessfully debugging code, for example. This repeated failure left me feeling like I'd been wasting time.
>
> Craving: I wanted a small victory. I wanted to feel like my time had produced at least some accomplishment, however small.
>
> Response: I consumed entertainment. I made some headway in a video game or finished some social media task.
>
> Reward: I felt a small sense of getting something done. Games, social media, and other distractions may be meaningless tasks, but they felt slightly more productive than hours of repeatedly accomplishing nothing toward my research.

Afterward, my self-loathing would generate enough willpower to get me back on task. But unless I hit an unlikely breakthrough, I would struggle to make progress, trigger the same problem-failure cue, and initiate the craving all over again.

By identifying that habit chain, however, I discovered two weaknesses I could exploit. The habit's first weakness: making progress in some entertainment is a meaningless accomplishment and a poor habit-reward. Second, the habit often ended where it started—working on a repeatedly-failed problem—which primed me to repeat the same problem-failure cue. I defeated this bad habit by shifting it toward a response that yields a more desirable reward and that minimizes the bad habit's reinforcing nature.

The other trick to breaking this bad habit was to accept that the cue and the craving were okay. Working on hard problems will lead to frustrating standstills. I couldn't eliminate that cue unless I stopped pursuing challenging projects. And achieving a small victory might actually help me stay focused; that small victory urge was a useful craving.

I used all of this information to replace the bad habit with a good one by making some small adjustments. First, I installed a browser application that blocks specific sites. Now, when I navigate to those websites, I first meet an intermediate page that says, "Entertainment does not give the small victory you are looking for. Why not do something more rewarding instead?" I can still click past this gatekeeper, but that intermediate page makes that response a bit harder and the reward a lot less satisfying.

Second, I kept the cue and craving but designed a better response. Now when I hit my repeated-failure cue, and my small-victory craving, I have a new response: I read something relevant to my research project. I enjoy reading, and I always have some book, article, or study wanting attention. That response produces a meaningful small victory—progress in my reading and note-taking. It also breaks the discouraging failure cycle because I abandon that difficult problem until my next deep work session and indulge my reading instead. That may seem like it would slow the project down, but I can afford the lost time because of my deep work philosophy. I know that my subconscious will be working on that difficult problem, so I let my conscious efforts rest. And since I schedule some deep work every day, I am usually ahead of my deadlines and free to solve that difficult problem without urgency.

Habit manipulation is not an overnight fix: it requires strategic design, takes time to implement, and cannot automate conscious deep work efforts. But habits are powerful tools that can bypass our unreliable willpower by automating many of the daily decisions that lead us to productive deep work sessions. Habits make our actions much more consistent. And when we align that consistency with our deep work priorities and our noble motivations, we create a well-rounded productivity system that can liberate our inner productive researcher. But to fully unlock that potential, we must take one more chapter to apply this productivity system more concretely to our journal publication plans.

4

Cultivate a Virtuous Cycle

The previous chapters explained three strategies for liberating our inner productive researcher. Question-motivated research helps us orient our work toward noble ambitions. A deep work mindset helps us prioritize actions that will pursue those research motivations. Manipulating our habits helps us fight distraction and access deep concentration more consistently.[19] We need these tools to become productive researchers that can complete the great amount of work needed to publish our first journal article.

But now it's time for me to come clean; I've been leading us on a bit. Although a productive researcher exists in each of us, we can never fully liberate it. It's an idealized version of ourselves, and its consistent habits, deep concentration, and clear motivations can never fully overthrow our less-productive personas.

But that's okay. Because the productive researcher is still worth aiming for: it's a good role model and a desirable identity. In the end, it doesn't matter if we *are* a productive researcher, but only if we are *becoming* one. That is, we become increasingly more effective as we approach that model identity, even if we never completely attain it.

Shifts in our researcher identity, however, happen gradually. Over time, we reinforce our new identity through the many small decisions we make each day. Every small action casts a vote for which identity we are becoming.[20] When our bad decisions outweigh the good, we reinforce our less-productive personas and fuel a downward spiral. In that downward spiral, our self-doubt inhibits our ability to choose good over bad, and our continued poor decisions exacerbate those doubts. But when our good decisions outweigh the bad, we reinforce our productive researcher identity and cultivate a virtuous cycle. In that virtuous cycle, our confidence strengthens our ability to choose good over bad, and our continued good decisions bolster that confidence.

To successfully finish our research project, we must cultivate these virtuous cycles. We can do that by applying the previous chapters' productivity strategies in specific ways to our actual work situations. That means we need to switch from discussing productivity philosophy to exploring some concrete applications: we need to identify some specific changes we can make to our behavior and commit to implementing them. If we don't, the research process—Part Two of this book—will be much more difficult to accomplish.

REDESIGN YOUR WORK RHYTHM

Let's take some time, then, to consider how you can use those productivity frameworks to design a new work rhythm that more successfully advances your research project. As a budding productive researcher, you'll need to motivate your project with a research question, prioritize deep work, and build better habits.

I can help you with the first two goals. First, I'll help you motivate your project by helping you to identify a research gap and develop a research question. The research gap will contextualize your project within the literature. The research question will orient your project toward an achievable end. Second, I'll help you prioritize deep work by defining deep research tasks for you to work on. As you work through Part Two of this book, I'll provide step-by-step instructions for completing the many tasks that will advance your research project.

So I'll help you develop the *why*—your research question—and the *what*—your deep research tasks. But unless our friend discovers that productivity potion, it's up to you to decide *how* you will get it all done: to figure out how you will prioritize deep work and build habits that will steadily advance you toward answering your research question.

Your task, then, is to redesign your work rhythm to prioritize deep work and build consistent habits. As you work through this chapter's technique for doing that, keep two constraints in mind. First, remember that your productive researcher persona emerges gradually; you cannot realize a virtuous cycle after a single planning session, but must regularly adjust your strategy. Second, you do have actual work to complete; you cannot constantly develop your productivity framework at the expense of advancing your research project.

To balance these two constraints, you'll devote most of your time to completing actual work but will regularly critique your practices during seasonal and weekly reviews. In seasonal reviews, you'll develop new strategies: you'll evaluate your trajectory and design plans to boost your virtuous productivity cycle. In weekly reviews, you'll make tactical corrections: you'll identify productivity shortcomings and make adjustments. These seasonal and weekly rhythms help to continually cultivate a virtuous cycle without derailing your actual work.

SEASONAL REVIEW

Every few months, pause for a day to design a new vision for your next season of work. In these seasonal reviews, step back from your work, critique your progress, and adjust your trajectory.

First, evaluate the notes from your last seasonal review. Compare the review's vision with your actual progress. How well did you implement your plan? What adjustments might improve your success? Which strategies will you abandon, and which will you continue?

Next, develop some ideas for increasing your next season's productivity. The following pages provide a template to help you do that. Think of the template as a starting point: it will help you apply the previous chapters' philosophies to design some initial productivity strategies, but as you complete more seasonal reviews your template will evolve into something more curated to your needs.

Regardless, the template's scope should persist: write goals that align with your productivity philosophy, compare your current behavior against those goals, and design actions to better pursue those goals in the future. The following template contains five goals, each with a series of elaborating questions. For each of these five goals, answer the questions to help you compare your behavior against those goals, and use those answers to create one action item.

Goal 1: Make Time for Deep Research: In your current schedule, when do you typically accomplish high-concentration research tasks? When is the most predictable, least-busy time of your day? How can you leverage that time to accommodate more deep work? When do you currently accomplish shallow work? How does shallow work currently interrupt your deep work plans? How can you push that shallow work to the fringes of your schedule without neglecting it?

Goal 2: Train for Deep Research: How would you rate your current ability to maintain long periods of focus? How might you challenge your brain to extend its ability to concentrate? What sporadic, multi-tasking, fast-paced activities do you regularly engage in? How can you consolidate those activities into something more focused? What high-concentration leisure activities can you pursue?

Goal 3: Rest from Deep Research: In your current schedule, when do you typically abstain from work? Does that provide you enough leisure time to feel rested and ready for work each morning? If not, how can you fit more downtime into your schedule? How would you rate your current nutrition, exercise regimen, and sleep quality? What small adjustments could you make to improve your diet? Can you incorporate more walking or cycling into your commute? Can you add an exercise session to your weekly schedule? How can you adjust your evening activities to support a more consistent bedtime?

Goal 4: Build good habits: What new habit would greatly increase your ability to make time for, train for, or rest from deep research? What is the cue-craving-response-reward chain for that habit? What cue can you design to initiate this new habit? What prize can you reward yourself to reinforce this new habit? What hurdles frustrate your ability to complete that habit chain? How can you manipulate that habit chain to make it more effective?

Goal 5: Break bad habits: What bad habit greatly stifles your ability to make time for, train for, or rest from deep research? What is the cue-craving-response-reward chain for that habit? What part of that habit chain would be easiest to break? Can you pivot the cue toward a more useful craving? Can you pivot the craving toward a more useful response?

Although the answers to these questions reveal insights about your behavior, the real goal of this template is to generate a list of five action items. This list translates abstract productivity philosophies into a concrete set of practices. That is, by implementing the items you generate with this template, you'll pursue actions that follow the template's productivity goals and ultimately align your work rhythm more closely with your productivity philosophy.

The action items below—outcomes of my recent seasonal review—illustrate some ideas that the template might produce. These items aren't prescriptive, but are merely examples of the types of practices you might develop in your review.

Make time for deep research: I work best in the mornings. But with my daughter starting preschool, my previously-productive 8:00-9:30 hours have given way to breakfast-making, clothes-dressing, and school-drop-off duties. To recover that morning productivity, I will shift that deep work session earlier, from 6:30-8:00.

Train for deep research: In the evenings, I consume too much screen-based entertainment. I'd like to expand my leisure time with a non-digital activity that requires some skill and concentration. I'll start memorizing music on my harmonica.[21]

Rest from deep research: Lately, I struggle to visit the gym, but I could easily fit more walking into my routine.[22] The three-mile walk to work is a bit far, but I can walk the one-mile route to the coffee shop where I work Mondays and Fridays.

Build good habits: To play harmonica regularly, I should build a new habit into my evening routine. The cue will be finishing my daughter's bed-time. The reward will be sipping bourbon[23] on my porch swing. To ease the response, I'll store the bourbon and harmonica near the back door.

Break bad habits: I have a habit of interrupting my work to check email. The habit cues when I suddenly remember an email I want to send. I respond by opening my email, starting a draft, and then getting distracted by my unread inbox. I will build a new response, where I write the email topic down on a sheet of paper and wait until my shallow work session to type it up.

Your final seasonal review task is to schedule your next seasonal review. Find a spot on your calendar three to five months from now and block out an entire day for it. Avoid busy weeks when possible—don't schedule your seasonal review during finals, for example. But defend the appointment even if your schedule grows busier than anticipated. Though you will often desire to free up some time by delaying the seasonal review, don't do it: your post-review productivity boost will recover any "lost time" spent on strategic planning.

At the end of this seasonal review process, you'll have some great ideas for improving your research productivity. But to make sure you carry out those action items, you must regularly check your progress toward achieving them. You'll perform that regular check during a weekly review.

WEEKLY REVIEW

Each week, pause for an hour to evaluate last week's success—to judge how well you pursued your seasonal review's action items—and make minor adjustments. Beyond calibrating your productivity progress, weekly reviews help balance your workload and prioritize the next week's tasks. As a starting point, consider accomplishing the following tasks during each weekly review:

Critique your virtuous cycle: How well did you implemented your seasonal review's action items this week? Adjust your practices to correct any shortcomings. If you're a data-driven decision maker, consider tracking some simple productivity metrics throughout the week: give yourself a mark each time you complete a new habit, finish an hour of deep work, or any other relevant accomplishments.

Check your work's progress: How well did you balance time between your different commitments this week? Check that you prioritized research, while adequately pursuing other commitments like coursework, extracurricular involvement, or other responsibilities.

Prioritize next week's tasks: What are the most important tasks for next week? Review your upcoming calendar and note important appointments. Find some tentative times for deep work sessions. Decide your most important shallow and deep work tasks—write them down to revisit on Monday morning.

These weekly reviews might feel inconsequential at first. Eventually, though, as you create productivity action items and as Part Two of the book provides specific weekly tasks, the weekly review will become a valuable part of your routine, crucial for keeping your work on track. For now, identify a recurring timeslot for your weekly review—perhaps an hour on Friday afternoon or Saturday morning—and design a habit that helps you consistently complete it.

WHEN TO MOVE ON

Part One of this book identifies some research productivity hurdles, develops a philosophy for overcoming them, and uses a planning template to translate that abstract philosophy into concrete actions. And after all of this meta-analysis of how to effectively get things done, you must be wondering: how do you know when you're ready to move on to Part Two of this book and actually start your research project? If you can never fully realize your productive researcher persona, how do you know when you've liberated it enough to successfully start your project?

The answer to that question depends on your current trajectory: are you following a downward spiral or a virtuous cycle? If you're in a downward spiral—dealing with anxiety, stress, or worse; making little progress toward your goals; indulging procrastination and distraction—then wait. Don't start this research project yet. Your risk of failure is high right now, and that failure may accelerate your downward spiral. Use your new work rhythm to tackle easier objectives, like getting ahead on coursework, catching up on reading, or mastering a new experimental technique. These types of small accomplishments might just reverse your trajectory. And if needed, find additional resources to help you break the downward spiral and get yourself on a better path.

If you're in a virtuous cycle—feeling optimistic, experiencing small victories each day, excited to tackle a large project—then proceed. Your risk of failure is low. You're in a good place to pivot potential failures into valuable lessons. And a research project will give you plenty of deep work tasks to train your new work rhythm on. The rest of the book provides everything you'll need to forge ahead.

Part One Recap

Before we begin our research project, we must overcome some barriers that might stifle our progress—we must liberate our inner productive researcher. To do that, we developed a three-part productivity philosophy:

> Motivate Research with Questions: To produce our best work, we pursue interdependence and begin with the end in mind. A well-crafted research question accomplishes both of these goals; our research question connects our research to the literature and guides our project toward an achievable end. A well-crafted research question harnesses our curiosity, promises social and scientific value, and seeks broad scientific application while respecting our limited resources.
>
> Prioritize Deep Work: To make progress toward our goals, we must prioritize the actions that advance them. We advance our research project through reading, experimenting, and writing—high-concentration activities that fall under the definition of "deep work." We pursue deep work by making time for it in our schedule, training our brain to concentrate, and resting each day.
>
> Build Consistency through Habits: To consistently accomplish deep work, we must develop habits that help us regularly pursue it. We develop habits by manipulating the cue-craving-response-reward chain. By adjusting our habits, we automate many of the small decisions that lead us to the situations where deep work thrives.

Though we cannot fully liberate our inner productive researcher, it is still a persona worth pursuing. We discussed two rhythms that help us to continually develop that persona. Using seasonal reviews, we translated our abstract productivity philosophy into concrete action items. These action items help us make time for deep research, train for deep research, rest from deep research, build good habits, and break bad habits. Using weekly reviews, we evaluated our productivity, made small adjustments, and planned our upcoming week.

As you complete more seasonal reviews, your planning template will evolve to accommodate your unique needs and to incorporate new productivity lessons. To expand your own productivity philosophy, explore some new ideas: ask what works for your peers, attend productivity seminars, and read more books—for example, the books highlighted in Part One:

Stephen Covey's *The 7 Habits of Highly Effective People*

Cal Newport's *Deep Work*

James Clear's *Atomic Habits*

You can also develop your philosophy by exploring a resource devoted specifically to academic productivity—my website:

www.ProductiveAcademic.com

PART TWO

From Research Idea to Publication

From Research Idea to Publication

A research project is an enormous undertaking that we will struggle to complete unless we develop a more productive work rhythm. Part One discussed a framework to help us do just that. Question-motivated research focused our project on noble ambitions. The deep work philosophy prioritized the difficult, creative, sustained actions that pursue those motivations. Good habits enabled us to minimize distractions and engage deep work more consistently. And regular planning sessions helped us translate those abstract frameworks into concrete practices.

As we pursue those practices, we will steadily complete the many tasks required to finish our first journal article—but only if we know what tasks to work on. The path from research idea to publication follows a complex, chaotic series of tasks. Part Two identifies those tasks and organizes them into a clear, step-by-step process.

Each chapter in Part Two discusses a unique phase of that research process. It describes the phase's goals, a chain of tasks for completing those goals, and the criteria for moving on to the next phase. Each chapter ends with a flowchart that visualizes its research tasks and a recap that summarizes its main points.

The research phase chapters proceed as follows:

Review the Literature

The existing literature provides background material for our journal article and, more importantly, establishes the research gap that helps us develop our research question. We'll explore strategies for reading, note taking, and organizing.

Outline the Project

Before we experiment, we synthesize our literature review, finalize our research question, consider what data will answer that research question, and design an experiment to produce that data. We'll discuss how outlining helps us avoid many mistakes in the experiment and writing phases.

Run the Experiment

With a detailed outline of our method, we calibrate our apparatus, run our experiment, and assess the quality of its output data. Though the technical details vary by field, we'll cover general, best experimenting practices and deal with common hurdles that prevent us from completing our experiment.

Visualize the Findings

Figures translate our experiment's raw output data into succinct illustrations of the project's most important findings. We'll use those findings to answer our research question and jumpstart the writing process. We'll use visualization theory to develop a figure-making checklist and use our colleagues' feedback to help us refine those figures into high-quality communication tools.

Write the First Draft

Working from our project outline, we'll combine our literature review notes, experimental methods, and figures into a unified story that answers our research question. We'll use storytelling tools to improve our writing's structure and flow. And we'll explore strategies for writing productively.

Edit into the Second Draft

The First Draft has all that our story needs to communicate its main points, but it needs editing to become readable. We'll discuss an editing process that improves the structure, paragraphs, sentences, and words of our article.

Revise until Published

The Second Draft gets reviewed by multiple researchers until it meets publication standards. We'll walk through the revision process and discuss strategies for handling feedback from our co-authors and from the anonymous peers that decide whether our project will ultimately be published.

These seven phases transform a vague research idea into a published journal article. Read the following chapters consecutively. By the end of Part Two, you'll have a complete roadmap for the entire research process.

Granted, the research process is less linear than this book portrays. Things go wrong. Experiments fail. Reviewers reject your work. Each phase is not completely distinct, and failures in any stage can send you back to correct earlier problems.

This is true for most of life. Randomness, luck, and providence influence your path. The best planning rarely unfolds verbatim. But without planning, you'll wander, make mistakes, and miss opportunities.

The same holds true for research. Attacking it with a good plan—even though it won't unfold as neatly as you hope—reduces the risk of major setbacks and puts you on the most successful path. So let's forge ahead through an imperfect but effective plan and get you published.

5

Review the Literature

Nothing drops your stomach quite like your supervisor telling you to redo months of unusable work. It brought me to tears. Well, I didn't actually cry. I only cry in movies where washed-up, old men receive some unexpected recognition to redeem their years of mundane struggle—when Arthur is honored by the Screenwriter's Guild in "The Holiday," for example. But there was little redemption in my supervisor's assessment of my poorly planned work that day.

My experiment-motivated outlook landed me in that situation. I left industry for grad school so I could nerd out analyzing energy systems. To me, research meant programming, data analysis, computational models—the sort of intriguing technical work that lures most of us to grad school in the first place. So when my supervisor suggested that I start my first research project by reviewing the literature, I obviously ignored the advice.

"Why do a bunch of reading when I can just discover everything first-hand?" I wondered. "Can't I just tinker around in the lab until I hit on something groundbreaking?" In my great wisdom, I tried that alternative instead. I learned to write an optimization program that modeled the electric grid. It was exciting—I relished engrossing myself in new technical skills. As a bonus, it's satisfying to work on a dark screen full of green-colored programming scripts; I'm really just manipulating spreadsheets, but I know that bystanders suspect I'm editing The Matrix.

A couple of months of this aimless, experiment-motivated research produced some results: findings that I called groundbreaking but my supervisor called unusable. Apparently, my analysis assumptions didn't quite hold, I used a dubious modeling method, and my research question had mostly been answered by other scientists. In short, the computational model was indefensible and the findings were unpublishable.

"How do I fix this?" I wondered. My supervisor reminded me to review the literature. Apparently, it would save me some heartache. How exactly, I wasn't sure. Another thing I was unsure about: how to actually complete a literature review.

The problem with literature review, like each phase of the research process, is that we understand it too vaguely. We underestimate its value and we lack a strategy for completing it. Literature review is just reading, right? Except that it's a nuanced, unstructured, monotonous kind of reading. Without motivation to do it or strategy to make it easier, we'll ignore our supervisor's advice and marginalize this valuable phase of the research process.

In this chapter, we'll develop a motivation and strategy for literature review. Using that strategy, we'll summarize individual journal articles as well as compile our notes across multiple publications to synthesize broader themes. At the end, we'll have a neat stack of reading notes and an organized literature synopsis. Those notes will sharpen our research question, justify our experimental methods, and jumpstart our writing and we'll use them to outline our project in the next chapter. An above-average literature review provides a strong foundation for each of the subsequent research phases to build on. So let's do it right the first time. It's worth the effort.

THE GOAL OF LITERATURE REVIEW

In the literature review phase, we search the academic literature—the library of published journal articles—to give our project context and develop its research gap. Thus, literature review connects strongly with the motivations in Chapter 1. It pursues interdependence by putting our project in the context of other researchers' work.[24] And by developing a research gap to inform our research question, it creates an end goal for our project. In fact, literature review is an incredibly useful way to begin our project; it jumpstarts our work in many ways.

Unfortunately, we may get a different impression when reading the average journal article. Many publications' literature reviews read as afterthoughts. In these articles, somewhere toward the end of the Introduction, we find a laundry list of citations and "et al.'s" that scattershot around the project's focus.[25] I suspect—because I know from experience—that such authors do their literature review between finishing their experiment and writing their first draft. Under that practice, literature review isn't a valuable exercise, it's a necessary evil to getting the work published.

We, however, will approach literature review with better motivations—not the feel-good, tweed-jacket, academic motivations that hold dear the literature's intrinsic value and impress on novice researchers how regular reading connects us to broader science and magically primes our brain for innovation—no, I mean more practical motivations. I'm asking what's in it for us?

For one, literature review makes our writing easier. We cite the literature in our journal article for five reasons:

1. to motivate our work and explain its social value,

2. to provide technical background information,

3. to compare our findings against other articles',

4. to communicate our project's scientific novelty by framing the research gap, and

5. to justify our experimental methods.

Each of these reasons ease the writing process by giving our manuscript some starting material; a successful literature review will write half of our manuscript for us.

Beyond easing the writing process, those last two reasons—framing the research gap and justifying our methods—ease the experimenting process as well. Gathering our methods from the literature helps us avoid costly mistakes in our experiment. Journal articles overflow with rigorously documented research methods. We should use them. In fact, the more we read, and the more we understand our field's various experimentation techniques, we can simply choose existing, validated methods for running our experiment.

Literature review also underpins a vital guidepost for our experiment—the research question. As we read, we find gaps in scientific understanding. These gaps represent missing knowledge, and we identify them by posing questions that the literature cannot answer. These inquiries evolve into our project's research question. And by building our research question around these gaps and answering it via existing experimental methods, we feel confident that our project can likely solve that research question, produce scientific novelty, and intrigue the researchers in our field. Put another way, literature review protects us from pursuing directionless experiments in search of ambiguous ideas that will either lead nowhere or lead somewhere that nobody cares about.[26]

So from a practical standpoint, literature review reduces our overall effort. It makes the writing process easier, reduces research mistakes, and helps us pursue a meaningful research question.

But we only receive these benefits if we review the literature methodically. The literature is vast. The days when one could read everything published in their discipline are long gone. Even the savants—those philosophers who unwind each night with a glass of wine and the latest edition of their field's specialist journal—know that we cannot simply wander blissfully through and absorb enough knowledge to magically stimulate our research. No, in this chapter, even though we greatly value the literature, we will approach it strategically and review just enough of it to defend our project and jumpstart its progress.

LITERATURE REVIEW BASICS

First, let's make sure you know what you're going to read and where you're going to find it. Your goal is to answer a specific question in a narrow niche of your broader research field. But you can't choose a research question until you have some notion of a topic or at least of a field that you want to work in. You may already have some research ideas, but if not, start your journey by reading some broader material.

You can develop your topic by reading wide. Ask your supervisor for some journals that target broader audiences. Grab a copy of *Science*. Find a relevant book. Then cozy up in your favorite coffee shop and wander around these wider publications to start envisioning where you could see yourself doing research. Look for topics that excite you. Identify developing areas in your discipline where new breakthroughs are more likely to occur. Search for problems with broad, rather than narrow application. This is not yet literature review, where you actively take notes and look for specific pieces of information in niche academic journals. This is just reading. Enjoy it, get lost in it, and narrow your way toward a research field that you'd like to contribute to.

Of course, your project might already be funded by a specific research grant. That's great, too. It might not feel as exciting as unfettered reading, but it helps when a research direction is simply provided—especially when you're just starting out. But that funding need not totally constrain you: if you understand the funding source, you may find plenty of latitude in developing a research question that aligns with the funding's intentions. Ask your supervisor for a copy of the funding proposal. Read through it. Get a sense of the research field. Learn some of your supervisor's motivations and research topics so you can develop research questions that they'll be excited to support.

Now, with a narrower topic, you're ready for deeper reading. First, let's discuss how to download a journal article: I didn't know how when I started and you might not either. Grab a citation from your supervisor's CV for an article in your topic area. Go to your university library's website and search for the article's title and the lead author's name. Click the link, find another link to where the article is available online, enter your login credentials, and download that pdf.

If you're having trouble, head to the library and get help from a real live librarian. While you're there, thank them—they do a lot of behind the scenes work that is rarely noticed. And thank the broader university library system for subscribing to all these academic journals so you don't have to pay $35 to read each article. Don't write a note to the library administration or anything. Just offer some tribute to the library spirits and be glad that you have free, easy access to the literature—not everyone does.

Of course, you'll want to read more than just one article from your supervisor's CV: you'll look through scores of articles before the literature review is done. But how to find these articles? Here are four ways to build your reading queue:

Browse an article's references. Start with one of your supervisor's publications, flip to the references at the end, and see what articles they cite there.

See who's citing an article. Browse articles that reference a publication that you've found particularly insightful. Search for that publication on Google Scholar.[27] Under the publication's title, click the link "cited by ###" for a list of articles that cite it.

Find a review. The literature contains some special articles called "reviews" that synthesize the existing literature for a niche topic. Good review articles are goldmines. Search Google Scholar for "review" + key words for your topic. Any articles with "review" in the title should be what you're looking for.

Search key words. A hit-or-miss tactic, search Google Scholar for key words. You can find key words in the articles you've already gathered. Many articles have actual lists of key words after the abstract—if not, harvest some key words from the articles' titles. Use Booleans—ANDs, ORs, NOTs—in your search and cross your fingers.

Browse every title. Read the abstract for any titles that look relevant. If the abstract seems interesting, download the article, rename it to include the author and title, and save it to your reading queue. You'll continue building your queue throughout the literature review process, but once you've gathered about twenty articles, you're ready to start reading.

DON'T READ; SKIM

The first time I read a research article was disappointing. I expected to be captivated, but I nearly fell asleep. Much of the literature is, sadly, quite boring to read. Though many researchers have exciting science to share, they bury that excitement with lackluster writing.

Luckily, by changing our reading mindset, we can avoid that boring writing without overlooking the exciting science buried underneath. This new mindset lowers our reading expectations to anticipate boring writing. In response, we stop reading and start skimming.

That's right—we won't fully read most articles—at least not from start to finish. Instead, we will use our new, more critical mindset to filter the literature. We filter our reading queue: we ignore most of the publications that we browse because they stray too far from our research topic. We also filter our actual reading: when we find a publication relevant to our topic, we skim its writing for useful information.

The exception to this skimming is when we read "exemplary articles." Exemplary articles speak closely to our research topic. They identify research gaps, detail useful experimental methods, or provide results that we'll compare our findings against. They are publications worth imitating; we will cite them often, so we'll make the effort to read them thoroughly.

Regardless of whether we're reading an exemplary article or skimming a publication for background material, we are fortunate that most articles follow a similar structure. Understanding that structure will greatly improve both our skimming and reading success.

TYPICAL ARTICLE STRUCTURE

Your main goal during literature review is to skim. Practically, this means distilling hundreds of pages of reading into a handful of well-organized notes. To do this, you will create two sets of notes. The first set summarizes each article individually by trimming its thousands of words down to a few pithy sentences. The second set synthesizes these summaries to help identify research gaps and develop your research question.

But before you create these notes, let's first define the typical journal article structure—the structure that streamlines the skimming and note-taking process. Disciplines and journals vary slightly, but most science and engineering publications share a common writing structure: Introduction, Methods, Results and Discussion. Also known as IMRaD,[28] this structure progresses through the following sections:

Abstract: what does the article cover? The abstract precedes the main text. It summarizes the Introduction, Methods, Results & Discussion in one brief paragraph.

Introduction: why does this research matter? Good articles answer that question in two scopes. First, they give broad motivation, explaining how the research addresses larger scientific questions or societal problems. Second, they give scientific justification, describing a research gap in their field and how the research fills it. This second scope may be written as a separate "Background" or "Literature Review" section.

Methods: how was this research accomplished? This section explains the theory, experimental design, apparatus, calculations, and statistical analysis used to generate the experimental data.

Results: what do the experimental data show? This section synthesizes the experimental output into figures, tables, and statistics. It points out trends, relationships, outliers, or observations that fuel the discussion.

Discussion: what can we infer from our findings? This section draws meaning from the Results to answer the research question. It places that meaning in the context of other academic work to widen the meaning to the larger research field. "Results & Discussion" may comprise a single section, in which case the facts will intermingle with the author's interpretations of the facts—it's important to distinguish fact from interpretation.

Conclusion: what does this article claim? The Conclusion ends the article by refocusing on the main point. It reminds the reader of the research question, the main finding that answers that research question, and how that answer connects to the Introduction's motivations. The Conclusion might have its own section header, or it might be an unadorned paragraph at the end of the Results & Discussion section. Regardless, it will be near the end of the publication.

That's the order you'll see many publications written in, but it's not the order you should read them in. Given your new-found skepticism about an article being relevant or well-written, your default tactic involves skimming only as much as needed to fill your notes. Reading an entire article from start to finish is an inefficient way to accomplish that. Rather, you'll want to skip around the article's various sections hunting for specific information. Let's discuss a note-taking strategy to help you do that.

TAKE USEFUL NOTES

Use the following note-taking strategy to guide your reading for each article. See the appendix for a note-taking template.

Or to create your own, list the article's title, journal, and publication year at the top of your notes. Add the following sections: Research Question, Motivation, Results, Methods, Impressions. Then start skimming the article:

1. Start with the Introduction. Look for the motivation and research question. The motivation is often near the first paragraph. It describes why the research is valuable. The research question is often near the last paragraph. It describes the specific goals of the research study. Write a one-sentence summary of each in your notes.

2. Skip ahead to the Results & Discussion. Look for the main finding, which directly answers the research question, and a few supplementary findings, which provide context and caveats to the main finding. A good article organizes its findings via subsection headers and figures. You can often use those signposts to quickly discern the results. If those aren't forthcoming, you might need to dig into the text a bit more. Many studies provide an overabundance of results. Keep the research question in mind and filter out the findings that answer it. Write a one-sentence summary of the main finding and each supplementary finding. Paste helpful figures to your notes. Synthesize the article's Discussion into a few sentences about how its results fit in with the broader field.

3. Flip back to the Methods. Good articles will start their Methods with a few introductory paragraphs that broadly summarize the experiment's different stages, how they interact, and what data they generate. That's

the paragraph you want to put in your notes. If the author doesn't provide it, you'll have to write it yourself. Most publications will at least have subsection headers to guide you, but every article will require some skimming to ensure that you understand the experiment. When you're starting out, it's tough to skim the Methods section because all research methods are new and complicated.[29] Eventually you'll recognize similar methods and skimming them becomes easier; many methods simply vary on a similar theme. Read enough to write a paragraph about the method's stages, their interactions, and the output data.

4. Read the Conclusion. The author should synthesize the article's main points here. An above-average manuscript will signal the Conclusion with a section header or a paragraph that starts with "In conclusion," but all articles—even if they don't explicitly identify a Conclusion—should have some sort of wrap-up summary near the end. Reading the Conclusion helps you verify that you understood the article. If you did a good job skimming, there should be no surprises here.

We started the chapter by identifying five things the literature gives our project: motivation, background, comparative results, methods justification, and research gaps. So far, the note-taking template addresses the first four, but we still need to explore the research gap. We cannot identify a gap by reading a single publication: we must look across multiple articles.

We can still ponder each article individually, though, and collect ongoing observations that will help us eventually identify a research gap.

This pondering happens in the last section of your notes: Impressions. Most of your notes are just summaries, but here you must stop and ask some critical questions about what you've just read. Go to the Impressions section of your notes and consider the following:

> How would you adjust the article's research question to better fit its motivation and research gap? What other aspects of the motivation and research gap are not being addressed by the research question?
>
> What findings would you add to better answer the article's research question? What limitations does the author identify about the Results? What seems strange about the data shown in the article's figures?
>
> In the Discussion, how do the findings vary from other studies? Do you agree with the authors' explanation of those differences? If not, what extra information would better explain those differences?
>
> What questions do you have about the experimental method? What part of the method seems underdeveloped? How could parts of the method be improved?
>
> What assumptions do the authors make? Do you agree with those assumptions? Should the experiment be expanded to abandon those assumptions?

Answering these questions might be challenging. Keep trying. As you read and interact with the literature, some questions, omissions, and gaps will continue to stand out. You'll identify these recurring weaknesses later when you use your notes' Impressions to synthesize your ponderings across multiple articles and explore the research gap.

After this depth of skimming, you're usually done. But occasionally you'll find an exemplary study that relates strongly to your research topic. These publications merit greater attention. Read them again, from beginning to end, and lengthen your notes. Over time, you'll reread these exemplary articles more than once, so don't burden your notes by summarizing their content fully. You just need enough detail to jog your memory and capture their most significant takeaways.

EXPLORE THE RESEARCH GAP

This note-taking strategy will help you read individual articles and produce notes for each unique publication. But you must read forty, fifty, or more articles during your literature review. And you must synthesize themes across all of them to identify your project's research gap.

You will accomplish this by keeping a second set of notes—a "literature synopsis." The literature synopsis simply compiles the high points of your individual article notes. It has two sections. In the first section, paste the one-sentence research question and one-sentence method from each article that you review. In the second section, paste your notes' Impressions. Each time you take notes on an article, paste those two items into the literature synopsis. See the appendix for a literature synopsis template.

Eventually, that synopsis grows into a ledger that critiques your overall literature review. Your reading Impressions lack meaning in isolation, but when you synthesize them, you'll begin to notice limitations, criticisms, and weaknesses that span multiple journal articles.

Those weaknesses stand out when you review your literature synopsis periodically. Initially, your Impressions will include many unanswered questions. But continued reading will absolve many of these questions—either because you gain some foundational knowledge or because you find publications that answer them. But as you keep reading, a few of those questions will linger. And the more you read, the surer you'll become that these remaining questions haven't yet been answered.

Those lingering questions bound your research gap. You can combine them and rewrite them in ways that identify an unexplored niche in your research field. And with that, you've discovered a viable research gap that you can use to create your research question, and you've conducted the literature review to support it.

A WEEKLY RHYTHM

The hardest part about reviewing the literature is its vastness. Its sheer volume discourages me in three ways. First, I doubt: I see all of these publications and wonder if I can really contribute something new. Second, I procrastinate: with scores of articles to read, skipping one reading day won't impact my timeline. Third, I dread: I see an overwhelming mountain of reading and cannot motivate myself to begin.

We must overcome these hurdles. The last part of our strategic literature review method describes a weekly rhythm that keeps this whole process manageable. This weekly routine has two features. First, it must help us pace ourselves. Literature review is relatively straightforward, but reading poorly-written article after poorly-written article is exhausting; it can take a lot of concentration to decipher the intentions of an inarticulate author. Reading more than two or three publications a day becomes unmanageable. Second, our weekly rhythm must let us periodically review our literature synopsis.

With that in mind, your weekly literature review routine should look something like this:

1. Each day, review the literature during your scheduled deep work time. Aim to skim two publications and take notes using the strategies in this chapter.

2. Augment that with a planning session at the end of each week. During that session, browse your reading queue, keep any articles worth skimming, and delete the rest. You'll also review your literature synopsis: reread your critiques and questions, delete any that you've answered, and consolidate the rest by common themes. Finally, pick ten articles to review for the next week.

WHEN TO MOVE ON

The beauty of this literature review process is that you get to pat yourself on the back each day for getting a bit done. You need not break new ground or find your research gap. But if you take notes on two articles, consider it a good day's work.

The problem with this process is it lacks a clear stopping point. You can endlessly find more articles, note them, curate your literature synopsis, and never finish.[30] Let's solve that problem by defining some criteria that tell you when to stop.

You're done with the literature review phase when:

1. All of the questions in your literature synopsis have been answered, deleted, or confirmed as identifying a research gap. Hopefully you have a handful of these unanswered questions so you can start forming a research gap around the most promising ones.

2. You've identified some experimental methods for exploring your research gap. Your literature review yields some example experiments. You can use those experimental methods verbatim or add minor adjustments. Beware the temptation to create new methods: experiments rarely run smoothly, and it's difficult enough to publish something without inventing a new method along the way.[31] Save those new method ideas for future projects, when you have more experience to handle the extra risk.

3. You've found a handful of exemplary articles. These publications give your work a foundation to build on. They support your project's reasonableness and feasibility. You'll want to find a few of them, at least.

Continue your weekly rhythm until you meet those criteria. In the meantime, get feedback from your supervisor. Though your supervisor cannot offer immediate assistance, I assume you have regular access to their guidance—for example, a standing monthly meeting. If you lack that guidance, identify a relatively experienced researcher—a research associate, postdoc, or senior graduate student—who can offer regular guidance and schedule a standing meeting with them instead. Then come to your supervisor meetings prepared: bring questions, confusions, and talking points.

The literature synopsis, in particular, provides helpful talking points for your supervisor meetings. These talking points help you approach your supervisor to discuss research motivations for your field, methods you have questions about, and research gaps you are noticing. And your supervisor can help validate that your stopping criteria are satisfied.

Wrapping up the literature review concludes the first phase of your research project. Your notes will help you write and experiment by motivating your work, providing background information, comparing your findings to other articles, defending your methods, and identifying a research gap. Those benefits will become more apparent in the next chapter, where you'll develop a research question, outline your project, and detail its experimental methods.

Chapter Recap

Literature review provides a foundation for our project. It eases the writing and the experimenting phases of the research process. We identified five practical uses for our literature review:

1. to motivate our work and explain its social value,

2. to provide technical background information,

3. to compare our findings against other articles',

4. to communicate our project's scientific novelty by framing the research gap, and

5. to justify our experimental methods.

To efficiently realize these benefits, we developed a strategic literature review method which prioritizes filtering and skimming research publications to efficiently populate our note-taking template. Each day, we skim two journal articles and take individual notes. Those notes include information about each article's research question, motivation, results, methods, and our Impressions. As we read articles, we compile our Impressions into a broader literature synopsis. Each week, we augment our daily reviews with a planning session to curate our reading queue and update our literature synopsis.

We discussed the following criteria for deciding when to move on from the literature review phase:

1. All of our literature synopsis questions have been answered, deleted, or confirmed as identifying a research gap,

2. we've identified some experimental methods for exploring that research gap, and

3. we've found some exemplary articles.

See the following page for the literature review phase flowchart. See the appendix for a note-taking template and a Literature Synopsis template. Download full-sized templates and additional resources from:

www.ProductiveAcademic.com/published

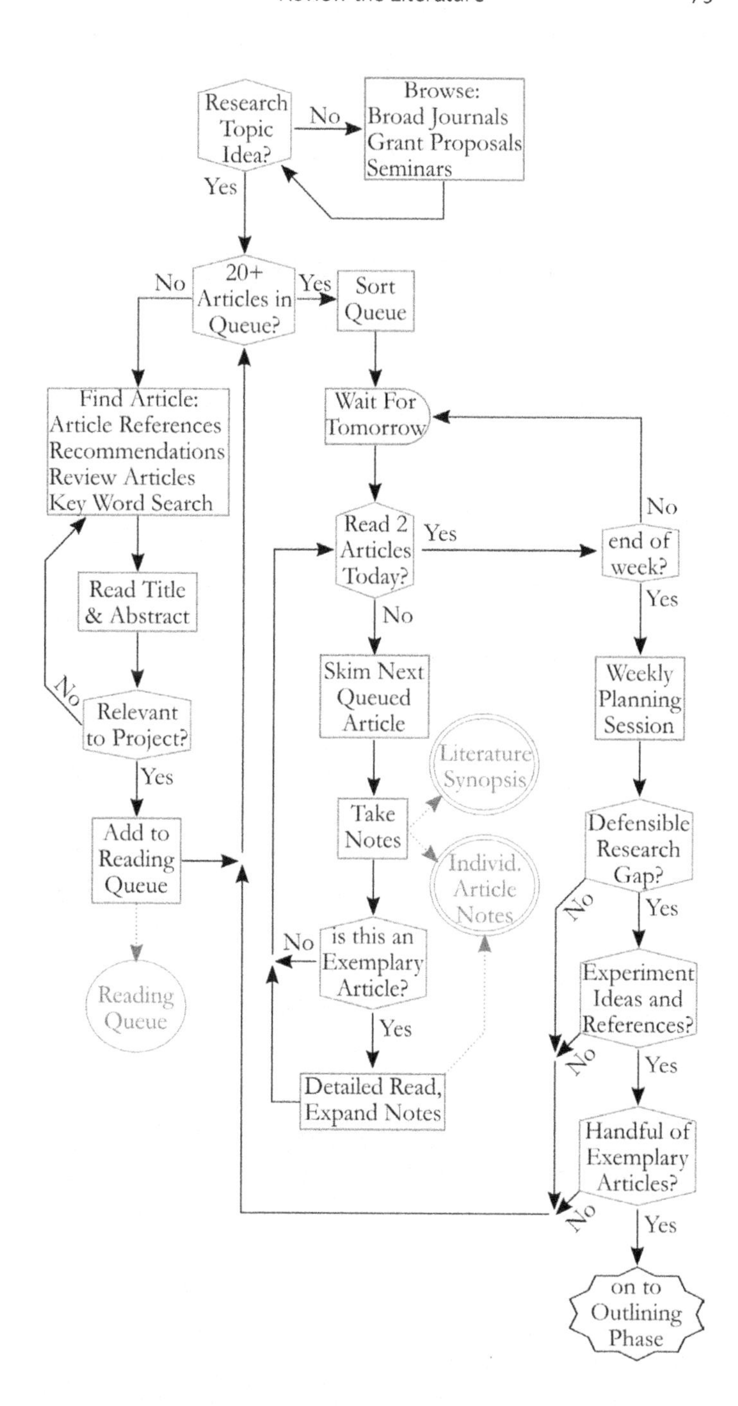
Research Topic Idea?
No
Browse:
Broad Journals
Grant Proposals
Seminars
Yes
No
20+ Articles in Queue?
Yes
Sort Queue
Find Article:
Article References
Recommendations
Review Articles
Key Word Search
Wait For Tomorrow
Read 2 Articles Today?
Yes
No
end of week?
Yes
No
Read Title & Abstract
Skim Next Queued Article
Weekly Planning Session
No
Relevant to Project?
Yes
Literature Synopsis
Take Notes
Add to Reading Queue
Individ. Article Notes
Defensible Research Gap?
No
Yes
No
is this an Exemplary Article?
Yes
Reading Queue
Experiment Ideas and References?
No
Yes
Detailed Read, Expand Notes
Handful of Exemplary Articles?
No
Yes
on to Outlining Phase

6

Outline the Project

Let's start this chapter with a horror story. It's my last semester of undergrad and I'm nearing finals week. I'm tense with the stress and anticipation that follows months of working on my senior project; the report still lacks some editing, but I'm excited to be done with it. I open my computer to make a few adjustments, but the report isn't there. My hard drive is empty. I gulp. I can't remember the last time I backed up my computer. I had so many opportunities to do so, but I foolishly pushed it off. And now I'll have to write the whole report from scratch.

Okay, that didn't actually happen. At least, not to me. But the story captures my sense of horror and foolishness resulting from a similar situation: failing to outline my research project before experimenting.

After completing my first literature review, I certainly felt more focused than when I had wandered aimlessly through experimentation. But instead of stopping to summarize my literature notes, I took that reassurance and jumped right back into the lab.

The longer I experimented, the less I remembered from my literature review. The results and assumptions of different articles mixed together. Various methods jumbled around in my head. And much of what I read I simply forgot. The outcome was a lot of re-reading and backstepping as I repeatedly corrected mistakes in my experimental method. And when the experiment ended, and I began to write the article, I so misremembered my citations that I practically had to redo the literature review anew. How foolish to leave that vital information to memory.

Writing an outline relieves our memory of that burden; it's like backing up our research project. Unless we outline our literature review now, we will lose much of that hard work to our poor long-term memory.[32]

Outlines, moreover, focus our jumbled thoughts into something more coherent; the outline-creation process refines, organizes, and details our project before it even begins. And when we craft our outline around our research question, it keeps our work motivated in the right direction.

In the outline developed in this chapter, we'll sort our literature review notes into the appropriate sections of our journal article, combine those notes into broader syntheses, develop our research question, and detail our experimental methods. At the end, we'll have a wordy but organized project outline that resembles an early draft of our journal article. We'll use that outline to guide our experiment in the next chapter and to jumpstart our writing two chapters after that. It might feel like one more hurdle keeping us from our experiment, but a good outline will save us from the foolishness of poorly planned methods and the horror of writing a journal article from scratch.

BENEFITS OF OUTLINING

Remember the goals of literature review: to motivate our research, provide background information for our readers, find comparisons for our results, defend our methods, and most importantly, to define our research gap. Those are useful goals that ease our writing and experimenting. But the loosely organized pile of literature review notes from the previous chapter can't quite achieve all of that. No, to realize those benefits, we must transform those literature review notes into a comprehensive project outline. But how does that help us?

For one, it captures our undocumented literature review perspectives before we lose them. There is a lot floating around in our head right now. We've taken good notes, but we have many unwritten thoughts that need to migrate from our brain onto paper. Outlining helps us capture those thoughts before they disappear. It helps us solidify our broad impression of the literature before we spend months experimenting and forget half of what we've read.

Outlining also organizes our research project.[33] Literature review provides a useful foundation, but our disorganized, loosely-connected notes hardly substitute for a systematic research plan. Consider how we would describe the current project to a friend. We could generally describe the research gap—that's a good start. But could we explain the finer details? How will we fill that gap? What data will our experiment generate? What methods will produce that data? We have only vague answers to these questions, and we cannot adequately elaborate them until we synthesize our reading into something more organized. So at the very least, we should outline our project to spare friends from our droning monologue about our underdeveloped experiment. [34] Even our mothers don't have the patience to suffer through such ramblings—they'll listen, of course, but they're only being nice.

Outlining also scrutinizes our experimental methods. Inadequate planning can severely frustrate our experiment. Experiments require significant effort; we cannot easily repeat them after discovering an error in our methods. A detailed experiment plan saves us from that drudgery and increases our chance of success.

Outlining greatly benefits our project. But like all phases of the research process, it can be a frustrating task unless we approach it methodically. In the next pages, we'll avoid that frustration by working through a step-by-step outlining plan.

REFINE THE LITERATURE REVIEW

Your goal for this chapter is to create a project outline—a document that resembles a journal article in structure, sorts your literature review into the appropriate article sections, and synthesizes your literature review into early versions of your motivation, research gap, and experimental method. The outline will evolve as your project progresses, but you'll make a complete draft of it now to get you headed in the right direction. See the appendix for a project outline template.

Begin your outline by creating an empty IMRaD structure that you will methodically populate. Remember from the previous chapter that a typical journal article follows the Introduction, Methods, Results, and Discussion structure. Use the literature to verify your field's unique IMRaD conventions. Then, start your outline by adding your field's particular IMRaD section headers to a blank document with some space in between sections for writing.

Sort the Literature

Next, you'll organize your literature review notes by sorting information into the appropriate IMRaD sections and synthesizing some broader takeaways. At first, this involves a lot of copying and pasting. Maintain a filtering mindset—you won't paste notes from every article you've read—although it's better to be generous at this stage and remove superfluous material later on.

Get all of your individual article notes in one place so you can easily flip through them. Open your notes for every study and paste any useful content—along with a citation—into the following sections:

1. In the Introduction, create a subsection header that reads, "What is the broad question being asked in my field?" For each article in your notes, copy the one-sentence research question and add a citation. You'll end up with a list of dozens of two-sentence summaries about what researchers in your field are working on.

2. Also in the Introduction, create a subsection header that reads, "Why is that question important?" For each article in your notes, copy the one-sentence research motivation. You'll end up with a list of one-sentence motivations that are driving the research in your field.

3. In the Results, create a subsection header that reads, "What main findings does the literature show to answer my field's research questions?" For each article in your notes, copy the one-sentence main finding. For exemplary articles—publications with particular relevance to your project—also add supplementary findings along with data, tables, and figures if helpful. You'll end up

with a list of the main findings in your research field along with the niche results from your closest peers.

4. In the Methods, create subsections entitled Procedure, Sample, Apparatus, Calculations, Statistics, Data, etc. These subsections are just suggestions—they are neither exhaustive nor required. For each article in your notes, take any methods that you might use in your experiment and sort them under the relevant subsection.

Synthesize the Literature

You must now make sense of all that copying and pasting by doing a bit of synthesis to look for common themes.[35] Currently, you have little more than a long list of referenced notes. By distilling them into something more cohesive, you can tailor these notes to your particular research project and develop some commentary that you'll use when writing your journal article's First Draft.

Work your way through the different outline subsections and search for common themes. Start, for example, with the Introduction. Under the subsection "What is the broad question being asked in my field?", read through the different research questions. What common ground can you find among these diverse research questions? What broader research questions can you write that capture the spirit of multiple of these referenced journal articles? Write three research questions that cover a majority of the referenced journal articles. Then sort those articles under the new research question that best describes them. Push the leftovers to a separate block of text—you'll likely delete these extras, but let them linger for now in case you need them later.

In the same way, synthesize other subsections of your outline. Look for common themes in the research literature's motivations, background information, methods, and results. Work through the different subsections of the outline, create two or three summarizing categories, sort the applicable referenced notes under the appropriate category, and move the leftovers to a separate block of text.

Although each of these syntheses adds value to the project, the most important subsection describes the research gap. The research gap and research question underpin your whole project. They deserve special attention in this synthesis exercise.

Define the Research Question

At the end of the Introduction, create a subsection entitled, "Research Gap". In this subsection, you'll refine the previous chapter's loosely defined literature synopsis into a concrete research gap and you'll target that gap with a research question.

Your literature synopsis notes contain a raw version of your research gap. You must refine that raw material into a tight, unified statement. Pull out the most interesting notes from the synopsis and rework them into a short paragraph that describes the research gap. That paragraph pinpoints a research topic that the literature currently overlooks. It answers the following questions:

What does the literature currently do well?

Despite those advances, what knowledge does the literature lack?

What is the literature missing that makes it unable to fill that knowledge gap?

An organized way to answer those questions is to choose three significant weaknesses from your literature synopsis and combine them into a research gap. These weaknesses might be experimental limitations, weak assumptions, narrow applications, caveats, omissions, etc. For each of these weaknesses:

1. Summarize the weakness.

2. Describe the research area, citing a few publications, where that weakness is most prevalent.

3. Point out how each of those publications exhibits that weakness.

Then, combine those weaknesses into the research gap. How do those weaknesses synergize? By adding all of those weaknesses together, what larger limitation is revealed? That larger limitation is your research gap. It tells the reader what the literature does not know. Describe that research gap in a detailed paragraph. Then place the finished research gap paragraph at the end of the Introduction section.

Writing a clear version of the research gap allows you to now define your research question. Simply put, the research question is an inquiry whose answer will fill the research gap. It must be succinct but still capture the project's breadth. Achieving this requires a bit of effort—revisit Chapter 1 for some pointers.

If you're feeling stuck, use feedback from colleagues to develop your idea. Recruit some peers for a brainstorming session. Present a literature review to your research group. Discuss your ideas with an experienced researcher at a conference. There are numerous ways to reach out to others for feedback, and with an outline to organize your thoughts and reduce your likelihood of rambling, you can feel confident of securing feedback from people other than your mother.

It can also help to brainstorm multiple questions: a main research question with some supplementary questions to add context. When the research question adequately addresses the research gap and captures the theme of the project, place it at the end of the Introduction section directly after your research gap paragraph. Make the research question stand out: highlight it, write it in bold font. It's a lighthouse in the turbulent seas of experimenting and writing. You'll look at it regularly during the research process to reorient yourself and avoid a figurative research shipwreck.

As an example, let's revisit our potions-making friend from Chapter 1. When we last left her, she planned to test whether a vinegar-cat-hair infusion might use trait-reversal to create a productivity potion. Reviewing the literature has helped her formalize this concept and expand its scope into something more scientifically novel.

In her literature review, our friend identified two weaknesses. First, the fur-infusion potions-making field has failed to create a productivity potion. Fur-infusion potions have successfully captured many desirable animal traits—improved memory from elephants, for example. Productivity, however, has been a difficult trait to capture: in two unsuccessful attempts, for example, researchers captured the beaver's hunger for wood and the draft-horse's desire to graze but failed to capture either animal's productivity trait.

Second, the trait-reversal field—whereby a sour solvent reverses the effect of a sweet-solvent-based potion—is largely unexplored. Our friend found only a handful of successful trait-reversal studies, primarily from the plant-based potions-making field. She discovered only one trait-reversal study in her fur-infusions field—a vinegar-pig-hair infusion that suppressed hunger.

Given these weaknesses, our potions-making friend identified a research gap: the literature knows nothing about whether a trait-reversal fur-infusion could produce a successful productivity potion. In fact, the literature knows little about trait-reversal potions in general, and almost nothing about trait-reversal via fur-infusions.

Given that gap, our friend's research question asks whether a trait-reversal fur-infusion can create a productivity potion. Or, more generally, her project asks whether trait-reversal can be achieved by fur-infusion potions at all.

This research question broadens the scope of her initial idea—to test vinegar-cat-hair infusions. She now realizes, given the lack of research data, that testing multiple hairs and solvents will make her project more scientifically novel. In addition to vinegar, she will use a solvent successfully used in plant-based trait-reversal potions—lemon juice. In addition to cat hair, she will use another hair successfully used in laziness-inducing potions—hair from opossums: notoriously lazy animals that sleep 20-hours per day—as well as a hair untested by the literature—sloth hair, which she can procure from a nearby zoo. This added breadth will increase her chance of developing a productivity potion and contribute more data to the trait-reversal potions-making field.

WEAVE YOUR PROJECT INTO THE LITERATURE

With some syntheses, a research gap, and a research question to work from, you can begin weaving the literature with the specific details of your own project. Work your way back through the outline and answer some specific questions about how your motivations, research question, anticipated findings, and methods interact with the literature.

Remember from Chapter 1 that a well-crafted project fills a gap in the scientific knowledge and improves society. Start by weaving your research question into the literature to support those two motivations:

1. At the end of the Introduction, after your research question, write the question "How does my research question fill the research gap?" The answer might seem obvious but remember that your readers will see the connection less clearly. You must make that connection clear for them. Sift through each aspect of the research gap and explain how the answer to your research question will address it.

2. At the end of the Introduction subsection entitled "Why is that question important?" write the question, "How does my research project improve society?" You've identified a research gap and proposed a research question that will fill it. Now consider how society might improve when you answer it. You can draw heavily from your research field's motivations. It's perfectly fine to share your peers' motivations. But it's nice

to have your own little twist if possible. What niche research topics might your project open up? What interdisciplinary connections would it forge? How might it impact technology or policy? Aim for enthusiasm without being grandiose: a good article—especially your first publication—need not revolutionize the world.

Now pause and consider your progress. You've done a lot of reading, summarizing, and synthesis to arrive at a well-motivated, well-defined research gap and a research question whose answer will fill that gap. Many experiment-motivated researchers labor through years of dead-end side projects to arrive at the same milestone. So display your research question somewhere prominent—maybe not on a tattoo or anything, at least not until the article is published—but cherish that research question. It represents your deepening pool of background knowledge in one succinct sentence. It's a motivational guidepost for your project, and it means you're headed in the right direction.

To conclude the outline, you will continue weaving your project into the literature by elaborating your Results and Methods. This last step is all about planning your experiment. You're about to jump into the weeds—the technical details that you've been salivating over since you accepted your grad school appointment. This last push takes some effort, but it will complete the outline and set you up to conduct a successful experiment in the next chapter.

PLAN THE EXPERIMENT

The last part of the outlining phase defines the methods you'll use in your experiment. You want a lot of detail about each step of the experiment plan. A detailed plan helps identify errors, missing equipment, incomplete calculations, or other hurdles. By identifying these hurdles now, before the actual experiment, you limit your mistakes and avoid wandering down unproductive research rabbit trails.

Begin with the Data in Mind

Experiments produce data.[36] Although generating data isn't your project's ultimate goal, you'll use data to produce findings that will answer your research question, which fills your research gap to advance science and improve society. But it all begins with your experiment's output data. So before you elaborate your experimental methods, you will brainstorm some anticipated findings, decide what data you will need to generate those findings, and then build your experiment with that output data in mind.

Go to your outline's Results section and hypothesize some findings for your experiment. Take cues from results in the literature. Brainstorm with your supervisor and other colleagues. Work out an answer to the question, "What experimental findings will answer my research question?" If it helps, you can break that question down into smaller components:

What cause/effect relationships do you anticipate?

What experimental variables might be important for showing those relationships?

Are those variables dependent or independent?

What other relationships, correlations, trends, distributions, comparisons, or compositions of those variables would you like to explore?

What is the main finding—that directly answers the research question?

What are the supplementary findings—that add context or give caveats to the main finding?

It's helpful to conceptualize your answers to these questions by writing about them, sharing your ideas with a colleague, and then drawing some draft figures. Make these figures clear: label the axes, plot the hypothetical data, note the relationships you hypothesize the data will show. Make as many of these figures as you want—this is brainstorming and there are no bad ideas.

Eventually, settle on a main finding that directly answers the research question, some supplementary findings that add context to that answer, and one or two figures for each of those findings. Then ask yourself what data you'll need to create those figures. Be specific. Include units. Make spreadsheets with column headers to hold your non-existent data. And now, with your output data in mind, let's design an experiment to create it.

Identify the Experiment's Stages

We have generally downplayed experimentation in this book: not because it's unimportant, but because we naturally tend to elevate it above the other research phases. But now, with our experiment at hand, we can relax that caution and lean in. Lab work, data processing, and statistical evaluation are, in fact, the most important parts of any scientific research project. They deserve a detailed, step-by-step procedure to guide them. Consequently, the Methods section will contain more detail than any other part of our outline. In this last step of the outlining phase, we will write a detailed experiment plan to reduce our mistakes and guide our experiment to produce the desired output data.

Sadly, our ability to dive deep here is limited. Research methods are the part of this book where you and I have the least common ground. But luckily, it is probably the area where you have the most mentorship, training, and confidence. Consider the lessons from your coursework. Reread the Methods from the exemplary articles in your literature review. Discuss experimental designs in your supervisor meetings. Use these resources to draft a dense experiment plan.

I am not, however, completely useless during this part of the process: I can offer general advice to keep you pointed in the right direction as you develop the experiment's details. Above all, keep these two questions in mind: "What am I going to do?"—in a literal, not an existential sense—and, "What data do I expect those actions to produce?"

Answer those questions for each of your experiment's steps. Experiments have many stages, and each stage produces intermediate data. In computational modeling, for example, one might query a database for raw data, clean that to produce input data, feed that into a model to generate raw output, aggregate that to produce findings, and statistically analyze those findings to inform conclusions. Each of these stages deserves its own answer to the questions "What am I going to do?" and "What data do I expect that to produce?" If the experiment goes well, you will work through this chain of steps and slowly transform the intermediate data into your desired output.

To help the experiment go well, collect your data using the lowest-cost, least-risky option. When designing an experiment, it is easy to underestimate the effort involved and the risk of failure. For your first project especially, avoid inventing new methods, seeking special access to proprietary data, concocting complex experimental sequences with many potential bottlenecks and failure points. Save these ambitious experiments for later in your career when you have better intuition about their risk and reward proposition. For now, try to repurpose methods from the literature, making minor adjustments if needed.

Now, with that background in mind, write your actual experiment plan. Start by defining your experiment's individual stages and developing the connections between them. You can do this with flowcharts, free writing, or by discussing with a friend. It can help to work backwards—from end to beginning by asking:

1. What data are you trying to produce?
2. What experiment can generate that data?
3. What model/apparatus can run that experiment?
4. What input data/pre-processing work does that model/apparatus require?
5. What technique can create/retrieve that input data?

Repeat that list of questions until you work your way back to a starting point. That starting point now connects—via a series of experimental steps and intermediate data—to your desired output data.

Elaborate the Experiment Plan

You now have a broad experimental framework. You've broken your experiment into stages with some ideas about their individual methods, apparatuses, and data. Now elaborate.

This is a good time to keep your literature notes nearby. Query the exemplary articles in particular, since you will use their techniques to design your experiment and will cite them often in your Methods section. Reread the exemplary articles' Methods as you develop your own. Understand what these studies did in their experiments. Learn from their successes and mistakes. And take cues from their experimental description and its level of detail.

There are many options for enriching your own experiment plan with more detail. Depending on your field's conventions, your Methods will have some mixture of the following, each of which deserves its own subsection:[37]

Variables: based on your understanding of theory, define which variables are dependent and independent, and which ones you will be controlling experimentally.

Measurements: describe what measurements you will use to quantify the variables. Decide how accurate and precise these measurements must be. Are you comparing variables within your own study, so precision and relative accuracy are important? Or are you comparing your measurements against other publications, so absolute accuracy is important, and you may require extra effort to pursue established scientific measurements?[38]

Samples: your experimental sample should represent the population you are studying and the phenomena you are exploring. How does your sample size balance uncertainty with laboratory practicalities? How accurately can you apply your findings to the broader population?

Experimental control, standards, randomization, and blinding: describe how you reduce bias. Based on the quality of your data, apparatus, assumptions, and random error in the experiment, what controls, standards, randomization, and blinding will maintain your desired accuracy and minimize opportunities for bias?

Replication: decide how many replications you require to achieve your desired confidence. Ask your supervisor and query the literature—do you need 95%, 99%, or some other confidence level for your results? Consider the phenomena that you're trying to detect, the accuracy expected from your research field, the statistical significance desired, and how many replications will achieve that significance. More replication will increase your confidence, but perfect confidence is impossible, and near-perfection is expensive, so choose a confidence level that balances rigor with practicality. Plan the experiment with that confidence level in mind.

Apparatus: describe the tools that will study the variables and produce the data you are interested in studying. Choose apparatuses that have been validated, are accessible, and can produce the desired experimental replication. Describe the theory behind each apparatus. How does the tool work? What physical effect—e.g., change in millivolts—does the apparatus actually measure, and how does it translate that measurement into output data? What errors, quirks, and aberrations can arise? How can you correct them? How will you calibrate the apparatus?

Procedure: describe how you will use the apparatus in your actual experiment. What inputs, adjustments, and tests will you run? What steps will you take to accomplish those? How will you record the output?

Data analysis: describe how you will analyze the experiment's output data. How will you translate the output data into the final information needed to create your results and figures?

If there's one place to let your perfectionism soar, it's here; you should err on the side of giving your Methods outline too much detail. Developing an extensive plan now can prevent many errors later. So work out the little details until the task veers toward drudgery. Then, get to a stopping point and be content with your imperfect but thorough experiment plan.

SUCCEEDING IN THE OUTLINING PHASE

A comprehensive project outline greatly eases the experiment and writing phases ahead. Outlining is, however, a difficult research phase to complete. It may feel like an unnecessary barrier to starting our anticipated experiment, and we can concoct many reasons why we might settle for a half-hearted outlining attempt.

We might be afraid of committing to an outline because we fear that it might change. True, our experimental methods and journal article manuscript might evolve as we work our way through the project. But we must work with an end in mind. A good outline, even if it changes along the way, will keep us focused, efficient, and on the best research path.

Outlines can also produce some disappointment. We may start a research project excited about a particular experiment but now realize that it doesn't suit our outline. We will always have more questions than we can answer, more technical interests than we can indulge.[39] Reckoning with that limitation—with our finite time, resources, capabilities—is one of research's great struggles. We might as well start dealing with that reckoning now.

Beyond these psychological hurdles, outlining is also difficult because it requires such deep concentration. Synthesizing literature, weaving our project into that synthesis, brainstorming on results, planning experiments—these all demand great mental energy.

Given these hurdles, the best way to succeed in the outlining phase is to first acknowledge its value and second to harness your daily deep work routine. Devote a couple of weeks of deep work time so the process isn't rushed. Work somewhere enjoyable where you can think creatively without interruption—like a favorite coffee shop, or maybe a favorite sensory deprivation chamber—whatever works for you.

Then slowly discover your ideas. Defend this time from distraction—turn off your internet and phone. But otherwise, do whatever seems helpful for encouraging creativity. Write. Draw mind maps, flowcharts, or other visual organization techniques. Go on a walk. Flip through literature notes. Discuss the project with a friend. Compare your evolving outline against relevant grant proposals and scope-of-work documents. Don't worry about blazing through the outline, about being highly efficient with this time; worry rather about accommodating deep thought and ending the process with a solid project plan that you're excited to work on.

WHEN TO MOVE ON

During the research project, your outline will likely evolve through many different versions. But you can wrap up the outlining phase whenever its first version is complete.

You're done with the outlining phase when:

1. You have a well-developed Introduction, some anticipated Results, and detailed Methods, all with plenty of citations for your First Draft manuscript.

2. You have enough information to run your experiment and you can adequately explain it to others.

Your supervisor can help you judge those two criteria. You need not share the actual outline document if its writing quality embarrasses you, but use that outline's content to drive some discussion during your supervisor meetings. If your supervisor can reiterate the project—the research question, how it fills the research gap, the findings you aim to produce, and the method you will use to get those findings—and they approve the project, then you've done a good job.

Great work so far. You've muscled your way through the academic literature and synthesized it into a nice project outline. You haven't written a title or abstract yet. And the Introduction and Results lack definition. But your outline contains the foundations of a journal article and the details of an experiment plan to create data that will generate findings to answer a research question that fills a gap in your field. You'll use that experiment plan in the next chapter where you finally get to run your experiment.

Chapter Recap

The outlining phase gives us time to capture our fleeting literature review musings, organize our project, and scrutinize our experimental methods. The finished outline will help us write our article's First Draft and complete our experiment with fewer missteps.

To help us write our article's First Draft, we created an outline in the IMRaD structure and filled it with referenced notes from our literature review. We took those notes, synthesized them into discussion points, and weaved those syntheses into our own project description. An important outcome of that synthesis process was to develop our research gap and research question.

To help us complete our experiment, we gave our outline a detailed Methods section. We started with our research question, asked what findings would answer that question, asked what data would produce those findings, and formulated an experiment to generate that data. We described each intermediate stage of our experiment and the data each stage will produce. We thus formed a chain of experimental steps that lead from some starting point to our final output data. And we detailed each step by describing its variables, measurements, apparatus, procedure, and other Methods components.

See the following page for the outlining phase flowchart. See the appendix for a Research Project Outline template. Download full-sized templates and additional resources from:

www.ProductiveAcademic.com/published

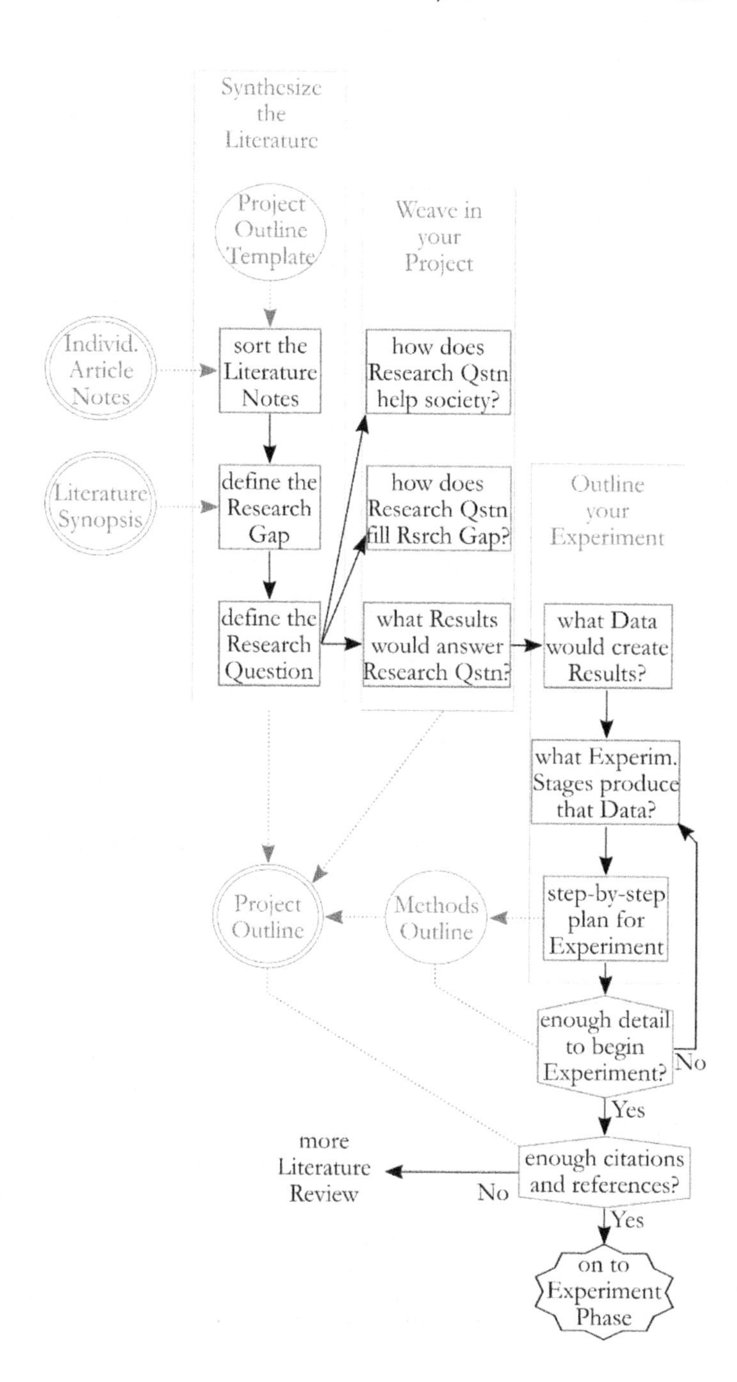
Synthesize the Literature
Project Outline Template
Weave in your Project
Individ. Article Notes
sort the Literature Notes
how does Research Qstn help society?
Literature Synopsis
define the Research Gap
how does Research Qstn fill Rsrch Gap?
Outline your Experiment
define the Research Question
what Results would answer Research Qstn?
what Data would create Results?
what Experim. Stages produce that Data?
Project Outline
Methods Outline
step-by-step plan for Experiment
enough detail to begin Experiment?
No
Yes
more Literature Review
No
enough citations and references?
Yes
on to Experiment Phase

7

Run the Experiment

Redoing my experiment the first time was entertaining. Redoing it the second time was a bit annoying. The third, fourth, fifth times grew ever exasperating. Experimenting was supposed to be the fun part of research, but as I revisited the same tasks to correct my mistakes it began to feel like self-flagellation: the lab was my monastery, and experiments were my daily penitence. I began to empathize with Sisyphus. Though, I suspect that the first time he rolled his stone up the hill, it wasn't exactly thrilling. This experiment, though, had thrilled me at one point, but that memory felt distant now.

During my first research project, I treated experimentation like a joy ride, like unfettered exploration, like answering the call of undiscovered science. And with some technical training behind me, I set off to blaze a trail. But my haphazard plan, limited preparation, and lack of direction stalled my experiment early on. The outcome: lots of missteps, backtracking, repetition, and fruitless rabbit trails that produced slow progress and repeated frustration.

It reminds me of the first time I explored a cave. It's good practice to pack plenty of food, a spare pickaxe, and some wood. It's recommended to mark one's path with torches, to note interesting junctions but prefer the more steeply descending route. But I let excitement dictate my first spelunking trip and entered the cave unprepared. Days later, hungry, lost, and without any iron ore to show for my journey, I sat in the dark with my notched sword, wondering how many more skeletons it could fend off.

That might have happened playing Minecraft rather than in real life, but the story illustrates the difference between exploring and wandering. Wandering lacks direction. It neglects preparation, follows whims, seeks intrigue. When we wander through experimentation, it's fun at first, but it eventually frustrates us with its lack of progress. Exploring, however, has an end in mind. It embraces preparation, follows protocol, seeks knowledge. When we explore through experimentation, it feels less serendipitous than wandering, perhaps, but it more effectively discovers new knowledge for our research project.

In this chapter, we'll explore, not wander, through the experimenting phase. We'll plan our experiment, develop a weekly routine to keep us focused, and use statistics to evaluate our progress. At the end, we'll have a wealth of output data, which we'll use in the next chapter to visualize our findings. For now, let's reward our patience by finally diving into the fun, hands-on, technical side of research—experimentation.

FOLLOW THE METHODS OUTLINE

In the last chapter, we completed an outline of our project that will ease the writing and experimenting ahead. The Methods portion of that outline includes a lot of detail—enough detail to complete each stage in a chain of experiments and produce our desired output data. All we have to do now is follow those Methods.

I thought about ending the chapter there. For one, you've built such a detailed, step-by-step outline that you really do just need to follow its Methods. Yes, you will hit unexpected snags and will need to adjust the Methods to accommodate, but that outline starts you on a successful path.

Additionally, and unfortunately, I cannot walk you through the experimental methods particular to your project. While many research tasks are relatively common among disciplines, experimental methods are not, and you're just as likely to being doing field work as laboratory work or computational modeling. Let your supervisor, coursework, and literature review guide you through the alchemy of your particular experimental techniques.

But we shouldn't end the chapter there, should we? No. What we should do is discuss broader aspects of research that apply across many different disciplines. Most of us run experiments on some sort of apparatus that requires troubleshooting. We all need to keep lab notes. And we all struggle with efficiency, consistency, and focus. So let's keep the chapter going and discuss those things we have in common.

LABORATORY NOTEBOOKS

Before we begin our experimental efforts, let's remind ourselves of a couple of things. First, remember our tendency for experiment-motivated research. We default to pursuing perfect experimental output, and that standard will cripple our progress. Second, we love indulging our curiosity. When we notice an aberration in our experimental data, stumble upon a new experimental technique, or see an interesting trend in our output, we find it difficult to ignore that anomaly; we will happily stall our main experiment to wander down that rabbit trail.

Our outline—the research question and Methods in particular—helps us avoid these temptations by focusing our plan on the immediate research project. But we need another tool to help us follow that plan—to keep us accountable to our outline. That tool is our laboratory notebook.

A laboratory notebook is simply a professional diary. Your research group may even have its own lab notebook protocols. If so, follow those. Otherwise, you can follow the conventional wisdom to keep your lab notes in an acid-free, page-numbered, hard-bound paper notebook using archival quality ink to date and sign each entry. It's good advice, especially if you're working on something patentable.

However, I personally struggle to keep physical, hand-written, paper-bound lab notes. Paper is slow. It doesn't have a search feature. I can't automatically back it up or store synchronized copies in multiple locations. I never took adequate hand-written notes for those reasons. So I keep digital notes instead. Beyond speed, accessibility, and security, digital notes let me insert data, images, hyperlinks, and other information much more easily than a hand-written notebook. Apparently, these digital notes hold less weight than hand-written notes in a patent case, but I figure, in my case, that a detailed set of digital notes is superior to a sparsely filled, illegible, misplaced lab notebook.

Regardless of your note-taking method, your lab notebook has two main goals: to help you track your research progress and to document your work so you can write about it in your First Draft. To accomplish this, make an entry in your lab notebook each day. Entries can be casual and long-winded. But write them in a way that can be understood years later. What exactly do you write in these entries? Here are a few ideas:

Record adjustments to your experimental method; e.g., the apparatus, sample, procedure, input data, etc.

Record your interactions with the apparatus; e.g., fine-tuning, calibration, adjustments, etc.

Narrate your progress. Discuss which tasks you attempted and completed today. Describe what data those tasks produced. Note which experiments you will work on tomorrow.

Display early output data or figures to observe the experiment's initial results.

Note your thoughts on how the experiment is going: whether you have questions or concerns, whether you noticed any strange results.

Whatever you write, be consistent. Lab notebooks require little effort but they can save you from gigantic blunders and help you stay on the right experimental path.

APPARATUS CALIBRATION

You will likely run your experiment on some sort of apparatus. Before you run any complex, time-intensive experiments, though, you should familiarize yourself with that apparatus.[40] Your understanding of this tool—of its accuracy, finicky behavior, and limitations—will bolster your experiment's success. Some initial testing and calibration now will help identify errors, miscalibrations, and bugs that would undermine your research project.

First, find some background information on the apparatus. Read any manuals on how the apparatus works. Dig a bit deeper into the theory behind its operation. Know what physical quantities it measures and how it translates those measurements into output readings. Learn the tool's different features and what happens when you adjust them. Know what can go wrong.[41]

Then calibrate the apparatus; run some smaller experiments to see if the apparatus produces the expected output. Start simple. Adjust one of the inputs. Predict how the output data should change. Keep working on it until your intuition is right. Move to more complex calibrations. Add new features to the tool. Use it to reproduce some data from the literature or from a lab mate. Tinker with the settings until you can reliably produce some known information at a small enough error.

Over time, your competency with the apparatus will improve. Your intuition for how each input affects the output will grow. Your ability to make small adjustments will sharpen. Once you feel confident with the apparatus, you can begin the actual experiment, but keep the following procedures in mind:

Work deliberately. Be systematic when adjusting inputs or adding features. Adjust the apparatus inputs one at a time. Leave the apparatus alone if it's producing adequate output.

Avoid untested changes. Re-calibrate the apparatus after each adjustment.

Develop a protocol. Develop a step-by-step checklist of operations that describe how to start, run, and shutdown the apparatus. Add this protocol to your project outline's Methods section.

Distrust second-hand calibration. I'm sure your coworkers are lovely people. You might trust them with your dog or maybe even with your children, but do not trust them with your apparatus. Trust only your own calibrations.[42]

A WORKFLOW FOR EXPERIMENTING

With your lab notebook and apparatus ready, you can finally begin the experiment. As you work through your outline Methods you must protect your efforts from some noteworthy hurdles. We've already discussed the tendency to wander through the experimenting phase. It's tempting to follow every data aberration, apparatus tweak, and other curious rabbit trails, but your project's efficiency requires that you stay on task. It's also easy to overwork during the experimenting phase; it's easy to spend long, odd hours in the lab, working far past your ability to concentrate. In these overworked states, you will make more mistakes, which you must later fix by inefficiently backtracking. To overcome these hurdles, you must regularly check your preliminary data, work on your experiment daily, and assess your progress weekly.

Preliminary Data

Hopefully, your experiment runs smoothly, but what do you do if it doesn't? First, you try to catch mistakes early by regularly checking your preliminary output data. Avoid interpreting anything from that output data just yet: you want to exclude your own bias from the experimental process, and you want to avoid manipulating the experimental procedure to produce output data that match your hypothesis—a disproven hypothesis is still valuable. But you should observe whether the output data look as expected, whether they meet the desired statistical confidence, whether relationships between variables make sense.

And when the preliminary data don't make sense, you'll identify experimental aberrations and respond to them. When you explore suspicious output data, you might:

1. Identify a miscalibration or error in the procedure or apparatus. If you find an error, you can develop a plan to recalibrate and rerun the botched part of the experiment. Run the plan by your supervisor and be glad that you caught the error early.

2. Suspect that the experimental method cannot produce your desired output data. Don't give up quite yet. Confirm these suspicions with some tests. See what your supervisor says. But if the method won't work, be

glad that you realized it sooner than later. You can repeat last chapter's methods outlining process and design a new experiment.

3. Suspect that you've discovered an exciting research tangent. These tangents often show up as outlier data: when the data break a trend, you don't know why, but you've ruled out experimental error. These tangents are exciting—serendipitous even—because they pique your curiosity. But you must hold off on indulging that curiosity. True, these tangents can lead to unexpected scientific discovery. Most of them, however, do not; it is risky to pursue them at the neglect of your well-defined, current research problem. You can explore these tangents later, but too many good research projects are derailed in pursuit of a risky, shiny distraction. For now, flag the tangent in your lab notebook, theorize some possible explanations, and refocus on the experiment at hand.

Periodically checking your output data helps you rectify mistakes early and document interesting research tangents without slowing your progress. You can also maintain steady progress and reduce your errors by practicing a work routine that reduces fatigue and reorients you toward your research question.

Daily Experiments

Experiments require deep work; we must follow detailed steps, troubleshoot errors, and document our progress. Given our limited daily capacity for deep work, we must prioritize experiments in our schedule to make sure they get the lengthy, undistracted attention they require. Maybe that seems obvious. In fact, experimenting is probably the one research phase where we most easily overwork ourselves to error-prone fatigue—we want to avoid that, too.

So we need to give our experiment enough time to be successful, but not so much time that they overwork us. A daily work rhythm accomplishes both. Daily work steadily completes the tasks in our experimental methods. And having that daily time for experimentation releases the pressure of overworking: we can save today's unfinished work for tomorrow. Experimenting fits in beautifully with the daily cycles of deep work we discussed in Chapter 2.

Experimenting requires many hours of work. It's tempting to ignore other deep work commitments while we finish our experiment. That mindset inevitably leads to stress when our experiment take longer than anticipated, and other important work falls behind.

So prioritize experiments, but save time for your other commitments. To strike that balance, consider the following:

1. How much time will the experimental task require? Do you require preparation before and cleanup protocols after your experimental work? Are there uncertain parts of the procedure that could require additional time? If so, account for these in your scheduling.

2. When should you schedule the experimental task? Consider what time of day you feel most motivated and your lab has the fewest distractions—i.e., chatty colleagues who, though often helpful with their feedback, can easily break your concentration during an experiment.

3. When will you conclude the experimental task? An open-ended task can drag on all day. But a whole day in the lab saps our brain's energy and stalls our progress on other work. Decide on some stopping criteria, and end the experimental task when you meet them.

Integrating experiments into your deep work routine will increase your efficiency, minimize distractions, and reduce human error. But daily experimenting won't keep you from wandering down rabbit trails that stray from your research question. To accomplish that, you must periodically resurface from the depths of lab work to revisit your research plan.

Weekly Assessment

Each week, you must remind yourself what you're trying to achieve and assess your progress in that direction. To do this, you will reconcile your lab notebook with your project outline. Devote some time at the end of the week for a brief planning session. Treat yourself to a nice coffee shop as a habit-building reward. And compare your lab notes with the project outline. Whenever these documents disagree, you must reconcile them by revisiting your experiment or updating your outline. Here are a few questions to keep in mind:

1. What changes did you make to the apparatus or methods that deviate from the project outline? If you can defend these changes, then update the outline to reflect them. Otherwise, consider whether the changes are appropriate.

2. What data did you generate this week? Determine whether those data reveal the variables, relationships,

and output you want to examine. If the data deviate from your expectations, ask whether the data reveal unexplained outliers that you should revisit later, or if they expose underlying experimental errors that you must correct. If you suspect an error, consider redesigning your methods to produce more accurate or precise output.

3. Does your research question still seem valid? Estimate whether your experimental data can answer your research question. If not, consider whether you should reword the research question, make it broader, make it more focused, or shift it in a different direction.

After reconciling your notes with your outline, plan the next week's experimenting goals. You don't need a rigid daily task list. Rather, specify some general directions: which parts of the outline Methods you will address and when you will schedule those tasks.

These weekly updates also help communicate progress to your supervisor. Not only do you have lab notes to discuss, but you have perspective on the project's trajectory: areas where you are hitting snags, tasks you think you've completed, and future plans. During your meetings, your supervisor can double-check these outcomes and help you maintain your steady progress.

In addition to keeping your project on track and creating talking points for your supervisor meetings, these weekly planning sessions have one final benefit: they provide regular opportunities to decide whether you've completed the experimenting phase of your research project.

WHEN TO MOVE ON

Experimenting may be the most engrossing of the research phases: we get to tinker with equipment, apply interesting technical skills, and explore intriguing research topics. But we must remember that the goal of experimenting is data. We experiment to produce data that generate findings to answer our research question. And we move on from the experimenting phase when our experimental data accomplish that task.

Our weekly planning sessions provide opportunities to assess the output data from each of our experiment stages. At the end of each experiment stage, we'll decide whether our experiment produced high-enough-quality output to move on to the next experiment stage or to end the experiment altogether and begin visualizing our findings. To move on, our output data must be two things. They must be meaningful. And they must be accurate.

Meaningful Data

To judge whether your output data are meaningful, you will infer some initial results, and see if those results provide enough information to answer your research question. These early, exploratory results can be simple or complex: you may average samples, visualize data, perform regression analysis, or implement machine learning. Whatever tool you employ, use these exploratory analyses to work from specific inferences to broader conclusions by considering:

1. How do different variables relate to each other? Identify causes, correlations, distributions, or compositions between your experimental variables.

2. What findings can you infer from those relationships? Consider what scientific knowledge you can derive from those relationships. Use that knowledge to answer your research question.

3. How do those findings compare with the literature? Scrutinize your findings versus the results from other studies in your research area. If your findings deviate from the literature's trajectory, attempt to explain those deviations.

When considering these questions, you'll naturally hope for findings that robustly answer the question and confirm your hypothesis. You will often get neither. But that's okay. Weak findings are still meaningful when cautiously interpreted and given appropriate caveats. And disproving your hypothesis can still lead to a meaningful solution. The goal is to answer your research question. If modest, unanticipated findings provide that answer, then be content to move on.

Accurate Data

Satisfied with the meaningfulness of your experimental data, you will now assess their accuracy. You want to defend your results by proving that your output data are accurate enough to support them. To test for accuracy, you'll typically use statistical analysis to quantify your data's confidence and error.

Specifically, you'll want to test your findings' statistical significance; that is test whether you can attribute your findings to scientific phenomena or just to the coincidence of random noise. Although scientific disciplines differ on the methods and standards used to make that judgement, most build on the classic concept of refuting the "null hypothesis."[43]

The null hypothesis attributes our findings to randomness: it suggests that the relationships between our variables, our data trends, and our inferences derive not from natural phenomena but from random noise. It is not a very nice hypothesis. And if we cannot confidently disprove it, then our findings lack the accuracy to be usable. Unless, of course, our research question asks whether the world is full of random noise—but I assume that article has already been published.

You can disprove the null hypothesis using a number of different statistical techniques: t-tests, chi-square distributions, analysis of variance (ANOVA), and other tools[44] developed by statisticians—those unsung mathematical heroes. Bless them. You'll use those tools to prove that your findings produce trends beyond what you would expect to see from random data. And that assertion proves the null hypothesis false.

These tools, however, have an important caveat called "confidence." You cannot disprove the null hypothesis completely. No theory explains the entire realm of nature. But you can be 99.9% confident. The same statistical tools that disprove the null hypothesis also provide the percentage confidence in that disproof.

You'll want just enough confidence to show that your findings can be generally applied. Often 95% confidence suffices. The required confidence depends on your research field's conventions, the statistical distributions behind your data, and the nuances of your research question.

As you assess the meaningfulness and accuracy of your data, you must acknowledge your field's conventions, the particularities of your data, and the scope of your research question.

You're done with the experimenting phase when:

1. You can disprove the null hypothesis with an appropriate amount of confidence—often 95% confidence will suffice.

2. Your preliminary findings appear to answer your research question. It's okay if the findings disagree with your hypothesis—that's still a valuable outcome. Consider the data trends, variable relationships, and other results. Do they make sense? Do they have practical significance? A small effect on an important societal outcome might be groundbreaking. A large effect with no societal value might be worthless.[45]

Once you validate your findings' meaningfulness and accuracy, you can conclude the experimenting phase.[46] But beware perfectionism. Perfect, indisputable findings sound wonderful, but all experiments suffer some amount of random noise. If your "imperfect" data disprove the null hypothesis and yield meaningful effects, then you're ready for the next chapter where you will use those data to generate figures that illustrate your findings.

LAST CHANCE FOR DATA

But before you move on from the experimenting phase, consider the benefits of generating a bit more data now, while the experimental setup is fresh on your mind. You have a good experimenting work rhythm. You have a calibrated apparatus. The marginal effort of creating new data is currently low. But later, when you're out of rhythm and a colleague has recalibrated the apparatus, generating new data will be more difficult. So if you want more data, now is the time to get them.

Why might you want more data? First, they may help during the revision phase—when peer-reviewers give feedback on your research project's quality. If additional data might increase the scope of your findings, add needed confidence to your output, or provide some helpful contextual information, then consider running a few more experiments.

Second, you've diligently pursued your research question and ignored rabbit trails—data outliers, unexplained aberrations, interesting tangents. Now is your chance to explore those rabbit trails further to see if they merit future research. You must continue to practice restraint—your main goal is still to move on to visualizing the findings of your current project. But you might briefly attempt to reproduce the rabbit trails, extend the data, and see if they hold under different experimental circumstances. Explore just enough so that you can revisit your notes in the future and decide whether these tangents merit their own research projects.

Chapter Recap

In the experimenting phase, we implemented our outline's Methods section to produce experimental data. We used that data to generate findings that answer our research question.

Successful experimenting requires steady effort: too little effort stalls our progress while too much effort yields fatigue-driven mistakes. We used a variety of tools to keep us on track:

Our outline guided our experimental procedure and connected us with our research question.

Our laboratory notebook documented our progress. We reconciled our lab notebook with our project outline to keep our project on task.

Calibrating our apparatus reduced experimental error and increased our competency with the device.

Checking our preliminary data helped us identify miscalibrations or inadequate methods early in our experiment so we could correct them without wasting significant time. Flagging interesting tangential data deferred those potential side-projects for later, which helped us stay on task.

Daily experiments made consistent progress and released the pressure to overwork.

Weekly assessments reconciled our progress with the project outline. They helped us set goals for the next week's experiments.

We discussed that we should move on from the experimenting phase whenever we can confirm that our output data are:

1. Meaningful: they produce findings with a large enough effect to make valuable contributions to science and society.

2. Accurate: they disprove the null hypothesis with enough confidence to meet the standards of our broad research field and of our particular research question.

See the following page for the experiment phase flowchart. Download additional resources from:

www.ProductiveAcademic.com/published

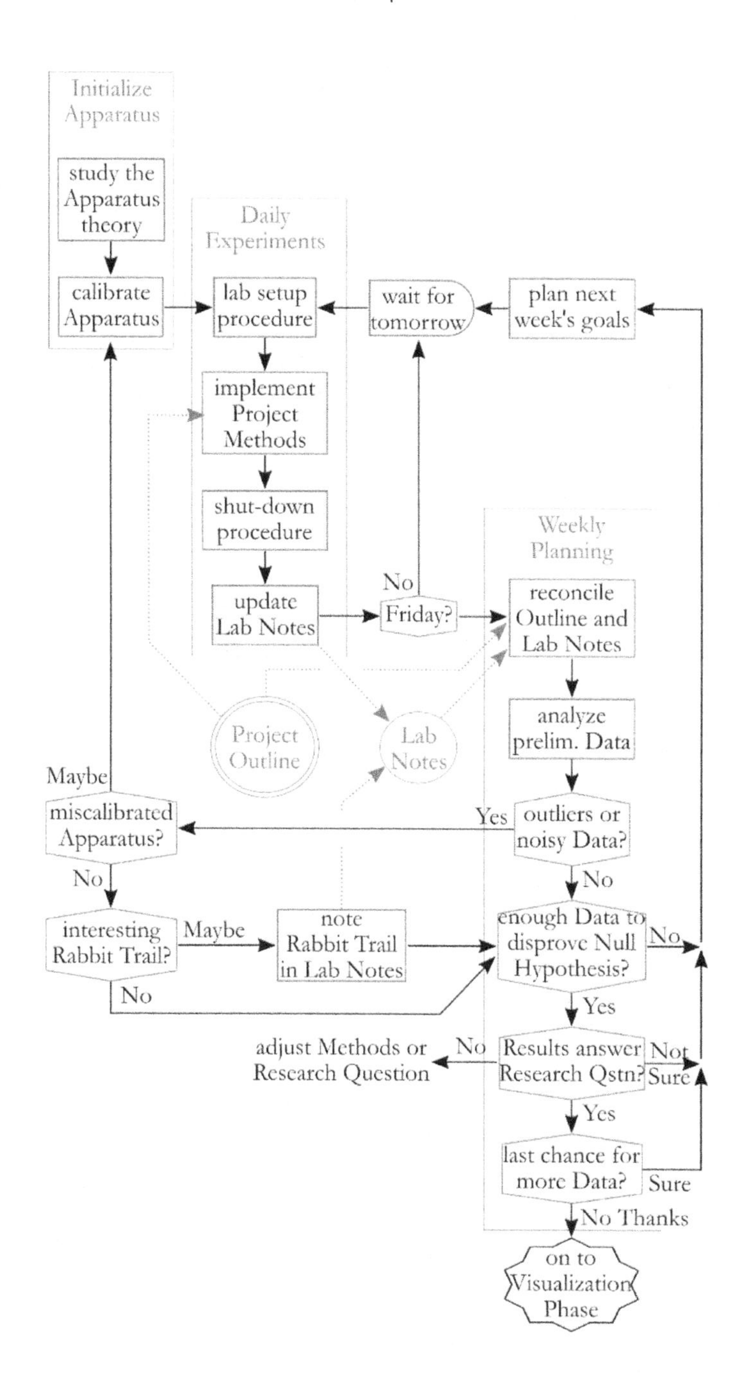

Initialize Apparatus
study the Apparatus theory
calibrate Apparatus
Daily Experiments
lab setup procedure
implement Project Methods
shut-down procedure
update Lab Notes
wait for tomorrow
plan next week's goals
No
Friday?
Weekly Planning
reconcile Outline and Lab Notes
analyze prelim. Data
Project Outline
Lab Notes
Maybe
miscalibrated Apparatus?
Yes
outliers or noisy Data?
No
No
interesting Rabbit Trail?
Maybe
note Rabbit Trail in Lab Notes
enough Data to disprove Null Hypothesis?
No
No
Yes
adjust Methods or Research Question
No
Results answer Research Qstn?
Not Sure
Yes
last chance for more Data?
Sure
No Thanks
on to Visualization Phase

8

Visualize the Findings

Poorly-crafted visuals produce two priceless facial expressions. The first expression, on the faces of the audience, manifests slowly as they scan the illustration and gradually determine they have no idea what the image describes. The second expression, on the face of the presenter, arises suddenly as they realize the audience's confusion. I've seen the first expression watching a museum's tour guide explain modern Picasso to school children. I've seen the second expression watching a conference presenter be interrupted to clarify the meaning of their chart's x-axis. And you could've seen both expressions simultaneously if you had witnessed the meeting where I showed my supervisor the final results of my first experiment.

In my early attempts at visualization, I crammed figures with as much information as possible. I wanted every image to deliver the maximum amount of material, and I wanted every article flooded with charts. The outcome of this strategy: the clueless expression on my supervisor's face, like a child bewildered by modern art.

Scientific figures are, of course, decidedly not modern art; they must avoid visual excess, artistic license, and cryptic meaning. No, scientific figures are communication tools that clarify our project's details. When we bloat our publications with an overwhelming set of confusing figures, we bewilder our audience and distract them from the project's main point. This is the opposite of communication. And unless we personally guide our reader through each figure's meaning—which of course we cannot do—then our audience will not know what those figures are trying to say. But when each figure succinctly describes one point, and those points clearly elaborate the project's main story, our visualizations become powerful communication tools that underpin our entire article.

In this chapter, we'll create effective, succinct visuals using a three-step process. First, we'll begin each figure by expressing its main point in writing. Then, we'll refine our charts using a set of figure-making guidelines. Finally, we'll use our colleagues' feedback to troubleshoot our figures. In the end, we'll produce a succinct set of figures that clarify our experiment's findings. We'll use those figures in the next chapter to support our answer to the research question. Building a high-quality set of figures now will clarify our project's story and jumpstart the writing of our article's First Draft.

THE GOAL OF FIGURES

Our research project is really progressing: so far, we've reviewed the literature, outlined the project, and completed the experiment. That experiment produced data that we'll use to create the findings that will answer our research question. But to get there, we must first convert that raw experimental output data into a meaningful set of figures.

A picture is worth 300 words. At least, that was each figure's contribution to my recent publication's word count limit. Even if a picture isn't worth a thousand words anymore, it's still a powerful communication tool that can replace a lot of writing by making visual arguments that are difficult to describe with words. Figures communicate complicated data and findings to our audience in ways that few other methods can.

Figures also drive an article's story. We can interpret a good article in terms of its visualizations: what do the figures show, what methods generated the data that built those figures, and why do those figures matter?

Yet despite the importance of figures, many publications skimp on visualization. Their cryptic charts take ages to decipher. Their cluttered data fail to make a coherent point. And their over-abundant illustrations distract from the research question.

We must overcome these shortcomings and instead produce powerful, succinct, and relevant figures that enrich our article's story. To accomplish that, we'll explore some visualization theory and develop a framework for applying that theory to our work. But first, we'll discuss the important of illustrating our findings with the right type of chart.

CHOOSE THE RIGHT CHART

We doom our visualization outright when we display our data with the wrong type of chart. Charts excel at communicating different kinds of variable relationships. Unless we choose our charts strategically, they may struggle to fulfill our intention.

To choose the right chart, let each figure illustrate a single finding. Then describe each figure's variables, relationships, and main point in writing. You'll use that verbiage to pick the type of chart that best communicates those relationships.[47]

Start with your main finding. You've already written about your main finding in your outline, but let's try to translate it into something more visual. Spend some time answering the following questions in writing:

> What experimental variables constitute that finding?
>
> How do those variables relate to each other?
>
> What relationships between those variables do you want to highlight?
>
> What data best capture those relationships?
>
> What will you interpret from those relationships?

Then analyze the verbiage of those answers to choose the chart that best conveys that kind of information. You can classify most of your findings under the following categories,[48] which will help you choose the appropriate chart:

> Comparison: use this chart type when series of data vary over time, when it's important to show trends, peaks, or valleys, when contrasting before and after an event. Comparisons are most commonly handled by Line Charts.
>
> Distribution: use this chart type when showing correlation between variables, when clustering data with simi-

lar variables, when individual data points matter. Distributions are most commonly handled by Histograms or Scatter Plots.

Composition: use this chart type when slicing a whole into its parts, when grouping related parts, when each part's contribution to the whole is important. Compositions are most commonly handled by Bar Charts or Tree Maps—a type of area chart comprised of rectangles.

That list may feel restrictive, but it covers a majority of what we see in academic publications. Fancier charts have their use, but until we master these basic forms, our attempts at complicated illustrations will likely confuse our readers. So let's start with the basic chart that best communicates our main finding and then mold it into a beautiful, persuasive figure.

VISUALIZATION THEORY

Having chosen the right chart type for communicating our main finding, we must design the chart to succinctly tell that finding's story. Visualization theory is a surprisingly deep rabbit hole, so we'll just focus on three concepts: how we view figures, maximizing our data ink, and minimizing our chartjunk.

Our eyes are trained to read words from left to right and top to bottom, but figures don't have a common structure for our eyes to follow, so we view them more interpretively:[49]

1. Our eyes notice high-contrast items first. We should use bright colors, bold lines, steep curves, and data clusters to highlight a figure's main point.

2. Our eyes can focus on only a few things at a time. We should limit the number of items in our figures.

3. Our brain seeks meaning from the relationships we see. We should use trends, intersections, and other relationships to focus the reader's interpretations.

Those points may seem a bit theoretical, but they provide helpful background for understanding two more easily-applied concepts from Edward R. Tufte's work on data visualization: maximizing data ink and minimizing chartjunk.[50]

"Data Ink" is the amount of ink in our chart that is used to display data. It is the points in our scatter plots, the lines in our line charts, the areas in our treemaps, and all of the axes, numbers, pointers, and markers that we use to give those items context. If we erase data ink from our chart, that chart loses some of its information. Within reason, we want to maximize our data ink: we want to erase non-data ink and erase redundant data ink so that our figures can focus on showing the data above all else.

"Chartjunk" is ornamentation that distracts from and can often distort the data ink in a figure. It includes complicated graphics, artistic use of depth, busy patterns, and thick axis grid lines. Basically, anything that distracts from the data. When we erase chartjunk, the figure's meaning remains unchanged. Within reason, we eliminate chartjunk so that there is nothing distracting our reader from focusing on the data and the figure's main point.

VISUALIZATION GUIDELINES

When we design a fancy original chart, we need visualization theory to make sure our audience understands our brave design. When we use more conventional designs like line, bar, and scatter plots, however, our audience already has context for how those designs work. Given that familiarity, we don't need deep visualization theory to help our reader understand those simpler charts. Instead, we can translate that theory into a handful of concrete guidelines.

For your first journal article, then, try and stick to the conventional chart designs and improve them with the following checklist:

The chart shows one main point. The highest-contrast data and most obvious trends should make that point. Some other, lower-contrast data can provide context for that main point. Any data beyond that are irrelevant and distracting. So highlight your most important data, de-emphasize with muted colors or lighter lines your contextual data, and remove the rest.

The chart has minimal text. Words can provide helpful context, but too many words begin to create their own visual effect that distracts from the main point. You must scrutinize every word in your chart and keep only those words that provide necessary context for the reader. If you can remove a word without changing the chart's message, you should delete it.

The text is understandable. If your reader doesn't understand the text, it becomes visual noise instead of helpful context. This misunderstanding happens often with acronyms and abbreviations. These shortened bits of text are tempting because they take up less visual space than full words. But if the reader has to look up acronyms by skipping back to the body of your manuscript, then you're making them work too hard.

Legends are used sparingly. Legends slow the reader down. They make the reader glance back and forth, away from the data to the legend's text, and they make the reader decipher which data belong to which legend entry. There are occasions for using legends, but avoid them if possible; default to putting text on the chart next to the data it represents. Then your reader knows automatically what they are looking at. And if you've culled your data to stay on point, you shouldn't have too many data series to annotate anyway.

The colors have meaning. Color is a useful tool because it can provide both contrast and context. Green for good, red for bad; blue for cold, red for hot; green for clean, brown for dirty—you should use these metaphors in your color choices. And you should also use contrast to highlight the most important data; your most meaningful data should be a bright color and your contextual data a light gray. Finally, choose color schemes that can be interpreted by the color-blind, otherwise you'll alienate some of your readers.

The style is simple. Using more than five line styles, data point markers, or other visual variety creates busy figures. The problem might be that you're showing too much data; you might not need five different categories of data to make one main point. If you do need that data, try a permutation of styles; for example, varying the blue/grey, thick/thin, solid/dashed combinations gives six different line styles using simple visuals that span from high to low contrast.

The grid lines are muted. We like putting grid lines in our charts because we think readers care about each individual datum and want to know every datum value. If that level of detail is important, consider using a table instead of a chart. If you want to make a figure with one main point, however, then each individual datum matters less than the important trend you're trying to show and detailed gridlines become less important. In many cases you can remove vertical grid lines, and significantly lighten horizontal grid lines. Then the gridlines cease to distract from the trends, intersections, or clusters you are trying to highlight, but still provide some context.

Pie charts are avoided. Our eyes struggle to interpret pie charts: we have difficulty gauging the geometric area of each pie wedge. To compensate, pie charts may show percentages or other numerical data, making them little better than color-coded tables. Pie charts also tend to require legends, callouts, or other text to distinguish each pie piece, which generates significant visual noise.[51] Use bar charts or tree maps instead. They communicate differences in area more effectively and are easier to annotate and scale.

The caption describes the main point. A figure's caption should tell the reader its main point. Filling the caption with information about the axes, series, or other context—especially if that information is already communicated within the figure itself—wastes words. Focus, instead, on pointing out the meaningful trends, clusters, or intersections in the data.

The y-axis starts at zero.[52] One can start an axis at a non-zero value to accentuate a slope, intersection, or other relationship. This misleads your reader, though. Such axes falsely portray data at the bottom of the figure as approaching zero. They exaggerate changes in the data's y-values. You should use a zero origin for your y-axis. If a near-zero datum value is impractical—like outdoor temperature on the Kelvin scale—you might deviate from this rule, but at least break the axis line or otherwise call attention to the non-zero origin.

Double y-axes are used carefully.[53] Double y-axes—where one data series uses one unit and scale, and another data series uses a different unit and scale—can also mislead the reader. Readers will assume that trends, intersections, and clusters between data on those different axes have meaning. But with a double y-axis, those assumptions might be incorrect. Consider that the intersection point between two differently-scaled lines will change depending on the maximum value of the secondary axis. Instead of double y-axis charts, create multiple, single-axis charts and stack them on top of a common x-axis.[54]

X-axes represent independent variables. Common practice places independent variables on the x-axis and dependent variables on the y-axis.[55] When you do the opposite, you imply that your dependent variables are independent or even causal.

Even that long list of visualization guidelines is not exhaustive. But it addresses many common mistakes seen in the literature. As you develop your charts, use this checklist to make them more succinct and more effective at communicating their main point.

TROUBLESHOOTING FIGURES

Figures require a lot of editing; it takes many different iterations to find a design that works. After you decide a chart's main point, highlight the data that make that point, and follow the previous checklist, you still need to verify that your figure communicates the correct information to the reader. You can do this by getting feedback from your peers and correcting the figure to address their misinterpretations.

Your supervisor and other colleagues can critique your figures much more effectively than you can. You know your figures too intimately to objectively judge whether they communicate a main point, use data ink effectively, and avoid chartjunk. But the fresh eyes of a friend provide unbiased insight.

So show each of your figures to multiple peers, and ask them the following questions:[56]

1. What are the first things you notice?

2. What are the main ideas that pop into your head?

3. What are some things you like, dislike, and wish were included?

Given that feedback, decide first if the figure communicates its main point. If not, what can you change to highlight points that your test readers missed? How can you de-emphasize things that the readers gave too much focus? How else can you respond to their feedback? Update the figure, get additional feedback, and continue revising until most people can quickly grasp the figure's main point.

If that feels a bit vague, here's an example. The pie chart in Fig 9.1 shows the sources of the 2017 U.S. energy supply.

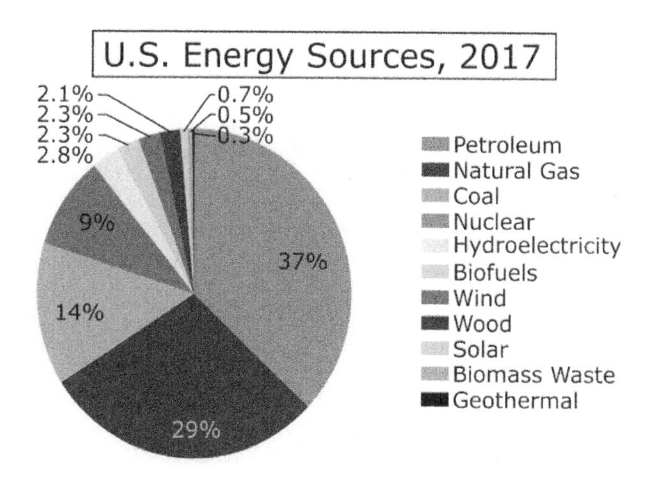

Fig 9.1: U.S. Energy Sources in 2017.

Suppose the figure's main goal is to highlight the small contribution of wind and solar to the overall energy mix. Our test reader gives us the following feedback:

The first things I notice: I see the two large pie wedges that dominate the chart, then I see the numerous small percentages clustered in the top left, then I look over to the legend and see that petroleum and natural gas are the big pie wedges, but I lose interest reading the rest of the legend.

The main idea that pops into my head: there are two big contributors to U.S. Energy supply—petroleum and natural gas—and a bunch of smaller contributors.

The things I like, dislike, and wish were included: I don't like much about this chart, actually. It has random colors, lots of text, an overwhelming legend, and the caption doesn't provide any helpful information. I also wish it categorized the sources a bit more—for example by whether they are renewable, fossil-based, low-emitting, or something like that.

Given that feedback, let's update the chart to better highlight the main point—the small contribution of wind and solar. The pie chart contains that data: if we know what to look for, we see that wind and solar make up about 3% together. But our reader isn't noticing that. Let's apply our visualization checklist and make a stronger version of this chart:

> Avoid using a pie chart. It's tough to distinguish the areas and colors of small pie wedges, and since we want to focus the chart on renewables—the smaller pieces of the pie—we want a chart type that helps us do that. Instead, let's use a treemap.
>
> Remove some text. If the actual percentages are important then we should just use a table. So let's remove all percentage values from the chart. Let's also de-emphasize the chart title—it's large, dark, boxed, and distracting.

Remove the legend. Jumping back and forth between the data and the legend is annoying. Let's remove it and label the data directly.

Choose a better color palette. The pie chart's random colors aren't meaningful and they add contrast to the wrong data. Let's use dark colors to emphasize the renewables—in a color version we might use dark green, since many readers will associate green with renewables. We can give wind and solar the highest contrast colors. Let's use light colors for the fossil fuels to de-emphasize that data. And let's color nuclear slightly differently—because it isn't a fossil fuel—but still de-emphasize it compared to the renewables.

Reduce the amount of data. Since we're focusing on wind and solar, we don't need to distinguish every other data series. We can, for example, combine biofuels, wood, and biomass waste into a new "Biomass" category without influencing the chart's main point.

Write a better caption. We don't need to reiterate the text from the chart title. Rather, let's focus on the story—the small contribution of wind and solar, maybe including their individual percentages.

The result is Fig 9.2, which communicates the main point much more clearly than the pie chart. It uses high-contrast colors to focus on wind and solar. It provides helpful context—hydro and biomass dominate renewables, petroleum and natural gas dominate overall—without letting that context overshadow the main point. It minimizes text, chartjunk, and callouts to keep the chart succinct.

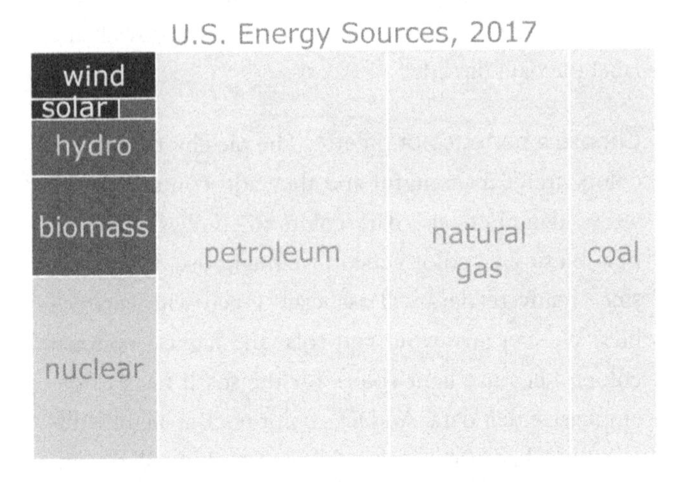

Fig 9.2: Wind (2.3%) and Solar (0.7%) contributed little to the 2017 U.S. energy supply.

We should still share this chart with more test readers and edit until it delivers a clear message to most of our colleagues, but that example shows how to use feedback and the visualization guidelines to troubleshoot an individual figure. To download more examples—in color—refer to the chapter recap.

For our next task, we will consider our complete set of figures, specify each of their main points, and decide how many figures we need to communicate our research project's story.

HOW MANY FIGURES?

If we tend to show too much data in each figure, we also tend to show too many figures in each article. These tendencies arise naturally when we're excited about our work. Every detail intrigues us; we don't want our reader to miss out.

The reader, however, perceives overabundant figures with less enthusiasm. To our readers, an article with numerous figures appears jumbled. They doubt whether the author has a main point. If we fail to balance our excessive figures with strong writing, our readers assume that we don't actually know the project's main point, and that we are spewing out data hoping that the reader will discern a main point on their own.

Excessive figures will clutter your article. But you mustn't overcorrect by including too few. How do you decide on the correct amount?

Begin with your results. You've already established in your outline a main finding with some supplementary findings that add context. Each finding deserves a single figure. If you feel the need to give a finding two figures, first consider whether you have used the best chart type. Then consider whether that finding should be broken up into two distinct results. As a rule, though, give each finding one figure; be judicious in adding more than that.

Beyond results, you may also choose to include some figures in your Methods. Are you using a complex, multi-step experimental process that could be better described by a flowchart? Will a diagram of your experimental apparatus help the reader better understand the experiment? Will a chart that shows raw input or output data help the reader understand the flow of experimental data? Such figures can help guide your readers through the Methods. These figures merit a place in your article.

Lastly, revisit your experimental rabbit trails. Is there any promising, unexpected data output, like outlier data or other interesting things that you intend to explore in future studies?

This article might be a good place to introduce those tangents. Your audience might find them interesting, and by introducing them now, you create an easy connection between this journal article and your future work, especially if you can use that tangent as a discussion point. Place such figures near the middle of your Results section, among the deeper project details, where they don't distract from the main story.

The figure count depends on your project's complexity. The rules above will help you tell the whole story without flooding the article with excessive visualization. After you've built your list of figures, created their designs, and edited them for clarity, you may be ready to move on to the next research phase and write your article's First Draft.

WHEN TO MOVE ON

Your figures will continue to evolve as you progress through the remainder of your project. Reviewers might suggest adjustments, updated findings might require new illustrations, and even "finished" figures will tempt you to improve them with some additional tinkering. But you can wrap up the visualization phase whenever you have enough high-quality figures to cover your project's highlights.

You're done with the visualization phase when:

1. You have the right amount of figures. You want to use as few figures as possible to tell your main story. Although there is no strict formula, start with one figure for each main and supplemental finding, and a few figures to describe the experiment.

2. Your figures effectively communicate their main point. Each figure should have one main point. When you try your illustrations on a test audience, they should understand each figure's main point.

Excellent work so far. You've translated your experiment's raw output data into a set of high-quality figures. When you combine those figures with your literature review, outline, and experimental methods, you'll have all the material you need to persuasively answer your research question. You'll begin that process in the next chapter when you write the manuscript's First Draft.

Chapter Recap

Figures are communication tools that translate experimental output into research findings. That is, figures turn our experimental data into findings that answer our research question.

To design an effective set of figures, we followed a three-step process. First, we verbalized each figure's main point and chose the best chart type for communicating that point. We then applied visualization theory to maximize data ink, minimize chartjunk, and create a checklist that we used to troubleshoot our design. Next, we sought feedback from our peers, asking them questions about each figure's dominant features, main point, and significant flaws. We used that feedback to update our figures and repeated that feedback loop until our test audience correctly understood each figure's intent.

We avoided flooding our manuscript with excessive visualizations by strategically using as few images as possible to tell our project's story. We created a figure for each finding, any complicated experimental concepts, and any noteworthy experimental tangents.

A high-quality set of figures succinctly shows the main findings of our experiment. After completing these figures, we will combine them with our literature review, project outline, and experimental methods to create the first complete version of our journal article—the First Draft.

See the following page for the visualization phase flowchart. Download additional resources, including a full-color figure troubleshooting guide from:

www.ProductiveAcademic.com/published

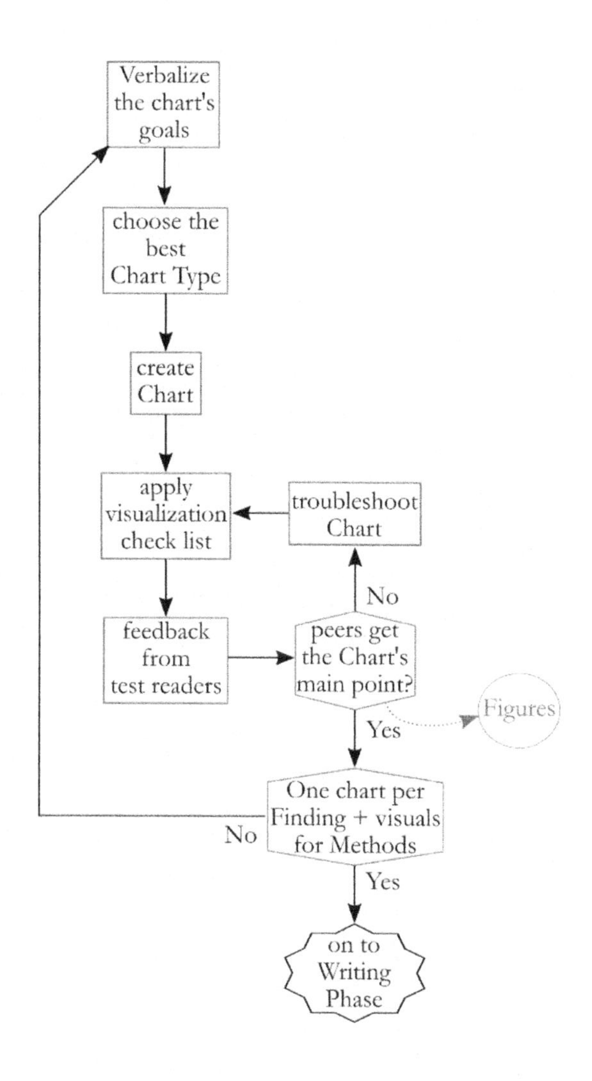
Verbalize the chart's goals
choose the best Chart Type
create Chart
apply visualization check list
troubleshoot Chart
feedback from test readers
peers get the Chart's main point?
No
Yes
Figures
One chart per Finding + visuals for Methods
No
Yes
on to Writing Phase

9

Write the First Draft

I was quickly becoming prolific at writing my journal article's first sentence. I had written and erased it at least fifty times. And each time I changed my mind and deleted my miniscule progress, I had to stare again at that passive aggressive empty page with its blinking cursor that questions, "Do you have any idea what you're doing?"

"No," I thought. "No, I don't know what I'm doing." Which was a bit of a surprise to me. I had written many technical manuscripts in undergrad and industry. But each sentence of my first journal article seemed a mile long. Everything I wrote felt strained. I spent a lot of time staring at the page wondering where the manuscript was going and how my bumbling words could ever capture the complex thoughts floating around in my brain. I would reread yesterday's writings, wonder how I could have penned something so awful, and rewrite it before moving on to new material.

It was like playing Candyland as a kid. In Candyland, you draw cards that move you slowly forward toward a finish line. Except that some of those cards undo your progress, knocking you back to an earlier part of the route. The worst card depicts Plumpy, a smug little troll eating a plum, who sends you back to the very beginning of the route. Well, I once drew that pompous little troll as I was about to win the game. I tore up the card, flipped over the board, and my family hasn't played Candyland since.

But I couldn't rip up the "Academic Writing" card. All I could do was inch my way forward, fighting for every small gain.

In retrospect, many things worked against my early journal-writing attempts. Pedagogically, I had little practical training and made rookie writing mistakes: I worked without an outline to guide me and I wrote and edited my manuscript simultaneously. Psychologically, I felt that my technically-inclined brain lacked the artistry to master writing. Emotionally, I worried that anyone reading my mediocre writing would doubt my research competency. I really didn't know how to write, I felt unnatural trying it, and I pressured myself into anxiety about it. No wonder it was so difficult!

In this chapter, we'll conquer those obstacles by demystifying the writing process. First, we'll incorporate the previous chapter's figures into our project outline. Then, we'll expand that outline using a formulaic approach that minimizes our stylistic writing decisions. We'll also discuss some techniques that professional writers use to avoid writer's block and to write more productively. Ultimately, we'll produce a rough First Draft that we'll refine during the editing phase in the next chapter. So let's forget our writing dread. We'll take this step-by-step and finish our First Draft as painlessly as possible.

THE GOAL OF THE FIRST DRAFT

We've come a long way through the research process; we've reviewed the literature, outlined our project, completed an experiment, and used the experimental data to visualize our findings. We've created all the material we need to persuasively answer our research question. Now, using the writing process, we'll combine that material into a unified, coherent story.

This story's First Draft is the earliest version of our project that resembles an actual journal article. It's much more than an outline, but it lacks the refinement of a peer-reviewed publication.

In fact, the First Draft is purposefully unrefined; we intentionally fill our First Draft with mediocre writing. The quality of our First Draft's writing should—per Anne Lamott's classic writing memoir, *Bird by Bird*—be "complete shit."[57] And that is truly the best word to capture our draft-writing mentality. Our early writing should be poorly written; the sound of someone reading it aloud should embarrass us. Our early writing can also be angry. Writing isn't easy. Cursing our way through it can help. Hell, we might as well freely curse in our First Draft. Don't worry—none of that shit will make it through editing to the final manuscript.

SELECT A JOURNAL

But before you do anything else, let's choose a journal to submit your project to. In fact, this is the latest point in the research process that you can choose your target journal. While many journals follow some close variation of the IMRaD structure, each will vary on their word counts, subsections, figure requirements, and other details. You'll use those details to update your project outline before you begin writing the First Draft. The benefit of waiting this long to choose your journal: you have a project outline, results, and a research question, which all help to identify your target audience.

Begin the search by consulting your literature review. Scan your literature review citations, note which journals they publish in, and flag any journals that show up multiple times—particularly the journals that publish your exemplary articles.

Select a few journal options, then view their websites. Journals will describe their vision statement, the type of research topics they publish, and other key words that can help you determine your project's fit. First, consider whether your project matches the journal's topical breadth. Does the journal accept a variety of loosely related topics under a larger umbrella? These types of journals prefer to publish broader studies that appeal to their wide readership. Or does the journal focus on a narrow topic? These types of journals prefer technically detailed articles that appeal to their niche audience. Where does your project fall in that spectrum?

Also consider each journal's "impact factor"—how often its average article is cited in its first two years. For context, check a handful of your literature review's journals. In my field, lower-tier journals have impact factors below 1, and higher-tier journals around 15. *Science* and *Nature*, for reference, both hover near 40. Don't publish in the lower-tier journals. It is rarely worthwhile to culminate years of work with a poorly-reviewed article in a journal that few people will read. Don't submit your first article to *Science* either. They will reject you. And each rejection, even the expected ones, can weaken a novice researcher's already fragile confidence. Your first journal article, and the bulk of your work for that matter, will target the middle-tier of the field—the respectable journals that have qualified reviewers, high standards, and a critical readership who will cite good work when they see it.

With topic and impact factor in mind, choose three journals. Give some reasons why each might be an attractive option. Discuss with your supervisor and decide on the first and backup options. It helps if these journals have a similar scope and a similar IMRaD structure: if the first journal rejects your article, you can submit to the second without completely restructuring the manuscript.[58]

Now that you have a journal to submit to, open your project outline, save a new version of it, and paste any of the journal's submissions requirements that affect the manuscript's structure. This includes section organization, word count, and specific instructions the journal might give on the writing or presentation of the research.

With your target journal selected, let's move on to writing the First Draft. I can feel your anxiety welling up. Don't worry, we'll save the actual writing of sentences for later. First, we'll discuss storytelling concepts, writing productivity practices, and paragraph-level outlining—all of which make sentence-writing easier.

SCIENCE AS A STORY

During the literature review chapter, we conceded that most journal articles are poorly written. Luckily, the IMRaD structure helps us skim bad writing for content. But we certainly prefer a well-written publication, don't we? When the writing flows and the main points are clear, we enjoy the article and will more likely read and cite it. Our audience feels the same way about our work. So while we can publish mediocre writing in respectable journals, above-average writing makes our work more readable, citable, and enjoyable.

The simplest way to elevate our writing above mediocrity is to tell our research project as a story. Storytelling may seem out of place in a scientific manuscript: we might associate it rather with fairy tales, ogres, and wizards. Although these types of stories seem unrelated to our serious research endeavors—except for stories about fur-infusion potions-making, of course—we can apply their underlying structures to improve our writing.

Whole books have been written about storytelling, and even about storytelling in science.[59] To keep it simple, we'll focus on two storytelling concepts[60] that can greatly improve our writing:

> One Main Point: The best stories follow one main point from beginning to end. Any side-stories are used to enrich—not distract from—the main story. In a scientific journal article, our main point is to answer the research question. Each section and result presents its own unique point that elaborates the research question's answer.

> Story Arcs: The best stories follow an arc. They begin by emphasizing broad, known information. They advance that information by providing narrower, nuanced details. They end by using those details to declare new, intriguing concepts. And those concepts provide new information with which to begin the next story arc.

The power of these two storytelling concepts is their applicability to all components of writing: articles, sections, paragraphs, and sentences all benefit from these ideas. Each writing component, for example, should make one distinct point. Each IMRaD section concentrates on a particular part of the article's story. Every paragraph has a single topical focus. And each sentence communicates one idea.

Likewise, the different writing components each follow their own story arcs. Sections typically open with broad information, narrow down into specific details, and then broaden back out to connect those details to the main story. Paragraphs open with a topic, provide additional sentences to elaborate that topic, and conclude by reinforcing their main point. Sentences first emphasize a known idea, add some detail in the middle, and end on something they want to emphasize. By enriching these writing components with storytelling concepts, we make them more effective.

To drive the point further, consider how often we see these storytelling concepts ignored. When publications make many different points, they feel cluttered. They have multifaceted research questions that require elaborate, fractal answers. They have dozens of figures that each vie for the reader's attention. They explore multiple side-stories that distract from the research question. The reader cannot unite the publication's many tangents nor discern its main point.

When publications ignore story arcs, they feel monotonous. Each paragraph makes an independent point without connecting to the paragraphs before or after it. The background information reads like a laundry list of unrelated literature references. Sentences bury important ideas in their middles. The article reads like a series of loosely-connected facts without a common direction. The reader cannot follow the article's flow.

It's quite easy to commit these storytelling mistakes. For one, we spend so much time with our research projects that we forget their complexity. Intricate concepts become familiar. Complicated stories seem obvious. Thus, we lack the perspective to adequately explain them. Additionally, we overestimate our reader's capability. We assume too much about our audience's existing knowledge, background context, and interest in our project. Together, these two misconceptions produce dense, unreadable publications that few readers will skim and fewer will wholly read.

Storytelling helps us combat these misperceptions and correct their mistakes. Our storytelling concepts—one main point and story arcs—provide a basic philosophy that we will apply throughout this chapter. We will use that these concepts to ease the writing process and produce a clear, interesting, persuasive First Draft.

WRITE LIKE A PROFESSIONAL

Now we begin a phase that you may have been dreading. There is something uniquely challenging about writing; our first attempts at putting thoughts into words feel so distant from the finished prose we want to create. Writing is an emotional, psychological, and practical battle. Its anxieties plague people of all professional disciplines, though, which means that we have a vast library of "how to write" books to help us minimize our writing struggles. So before you write, let's take a moment to discuss some professional writers' advice on how to overcome these challenges.

We've actually discussed two pieces of advice already. The first advice: rely on storytelling concepts for style. We mentioned two storytelling concepts and applied them specifically to scientific research. We follow one main point, arc our stories, and apply those concepts to each writing component. These guidelines take pressure off of our creativity by making our writing style a bit more prescriptive.

We also introduced the idea of the poorly-written First Draft. A deeper concept underpins this idea: write and edit at different times. It's natural, however, to write and edit simultaneously. As we write, we read, and we can't help but critique. But writing and editing are different skills; writing generates words, editing reorganizes them. So we must separate the two to avoid the inefficiency and frustration that comes from constantly creating and reorganizing at the same time. A helpful way to separate them: drastically lower our First Draft writing standards. When we aim for a poorly-written First Draft, we downplay our temptation to edit. It's okay if our First Draft needs massive editing. We just need to get words on paper for now, so we'll have something to edit later.

Another professional writing trick: write every day.[61] Though writing can occasionally feel serendipitous, it's usually just mundane. When we wait for inspiration, our progress slows. When we lag too far, we must binge write to meet deadlines, and binge writing produces bad results, burnout, and misery.[62] In fact, the best way to find inspiration, not to mention avoid binge writing, is to write every day.[63] When we incorporate writing into our daily deep work schedule, we make small, regular progress that adds up over time to big achievements—like publishing a journal article.

Finally, one last tip greatly simplifies the writing process: use the paragraph as the main component of writing.[64] We tend to view sentences as the main component of writing. But that viewpoint puts us under a lot of pressure. First, because our writing has so many sentences. Second, because sentences are so hard to get right: they risk numerous grammatical, vocabulary, and punctuation errors. Paragraphs, on the other hand, are fewer and simpler than sentences. If each paragraph in our writing has a main point, and those main points flow from one paragraph to the next, then our manuscript will flow. Sections merely categorize our paragraphs into helpful groups. Sentences merely elaborate them. And paragraphs can survive a poorly-written sentence here and there.

We will use these tips from the professionals to make our writing as painless as possible. In fact, when we follow these tips, we might even find we enjoy writing. But let's keep that to ourselves: anxious writers hate when someone ruins their solidarity.

WRITE THE FIRST DRAFT: PARAGRAPHS

If paragraphs are the main component of writing, then we ought to start our First Draft there. To focus our initial writing efforts on paragraphs, we will spend the next few pages developing a paragraph outline. The paragraph outline arranges each of the journal article's paragraphs. For each paragraph, we'll write a preliminary topic sentence and jot a few notes.[65] That basic structure will organize the article and jumpstart our sentence-writing in the next section.

So far, your research project is embodied in a project outline, your lab notes, and some visualizations. The paragraph outline unites those artifacts into a single document; it uses their information to create topic sentences and notes for each of the article's paragraphs. Those topic sentences declare each paragraph's main point. The notes elaborate the main point by describing intricacies, details, caveats, and other information that help explain the main point to your reader.

Maybe you're wondering what this paragraph outline looks like, exactly. I'd like to provide a template. But the problem with a template is that there are many ways to write a journal article. A highly-detailed template might offer precise instruction, but it will surely deviate from some aspect of your discipline's journal-writing norms. A less-detailed template might have broader application, but will lack some helpful complexity.

So instead of providing a template, I decided to provide three templates. The first template outlines each of the article's sections and describes some frameworks to help you develop each section's paragraphs. The second template outlines each of the article's paragraphs and provides some guidance to help you write each paragraph's topic sentence. The third template is in the book's appendix—it's a paragraph-by-paragraph outline with a bit of extra guidance.

These three templates strike a balance between general application and precise instruction that I hope you'll find useful. The added bonus is that you can pick the template that works best with your own style: if the appendix template feels heavy-handed, try the section-level template instead.

Regardless of which template you use, write the Results and Methods first—since visualization and experimentation are fresh on your mind—and the Introduction, Discussion, and Conclusion last—since they build on the writing in the Results and Methods sections. Finally, remember the goal of the paragraph outline: topic sentences and a few notes for each of the article's paragraphs. Resist the urge to fill your paragraphs with sentences—you'll do plenty of that in the next section.

A Section-level Template

The following template divides a scientific journal article into eleven sections. For each section, the template defines a goal and provides notes to help you organize the section's paragraphs and write their topic sentences.

1. Introduction

Jumpstart the Introduction by reviewing your project outline. In the project outline's Introduction section, you've already compiled some motivations and literature review. Review those notes now in light of your experiment's findings to form a complete vision of your research project—your motivation, research gap, research question, and the findings that answer that question.

With that vision in mind, write the Introduction's paragraph topic sentences. Although the Introduction's structure may vary by discipline, the main goals remain: motivate the project, identify the research gap, and describe the research question. You'll also reference literature here that you'll cite later for defending the experiment and discussing the findings. You can accomplish those goals using the following structure:

1.1 Motivation Paragraphs: describe the broad social value that your narrow research project might produce. Use your paragraphs to funnel from a broad motivation to your narrow research topic. For example, indicate a broad problem, describe a narrow component of that problem, discuss how that narrow problem component is solved by your niche research field, and explain how your niche research field is enhanced by your specific research topic. After finishing these paragraphs, your reader should know your topic area, your research field, and the broad social impact you hope to address.

1.2 Background/Literature Review Section: describe the academic literature's strengths and weaknesses.[66] To begin, cite some exemplary articles to summarize the literature's current progress in your research topic. Then introduce the weaknesses you will identify in subsequent paragraphs. For each weakness, describe a specific research area where that weakness exists, cite some key publications in that research area, describe those publication's omissions, caveats, and limitations, and discuss how those shortcomings illustrate the weakness. Prioritize citing articles that you'll reference in your Methods or Discussion sections. After finishing these paragraphs, your reader should see that the literature has made progress in your research topic area, but that it must overcome a few weaknesses if it hopes to progress further.

1.3 Research Question Paragraphs: use the literature weaknesses to synthesize a research gap, develop a research question, and—depending on your field—offer a hypothesis. The research gap describes what science does not yet know. The research question describes how you intend to fill that research gap. The hypothesis posits an answer to your research question. After finishing these paragraphs, the reader should know your research question and understand why that question has scientific novelty.

1.4 Closing Paragraphs: quickly reiterate the Introduction in reverse. Remind the reader how your research question fills the research gap and why filling that gap will improve science and society.

2. Methods

Begin the Methods by reviewing your laboratory notes and project outline. In the outlining phase, you developed a detailed experimental procedure. In the experimenting phase, you applied that procedure, recorded progress in your lab notes, and periodically reconciled those lab notes with the project outline's Methods section. Those lengthy, procedural documents contain all the information you need to write your article's Methods section, but you must winnow them down into a succinct discussion that your readers can actually digest.

The Methods section's main goal is to persuade the reader of your experiment's validity. Specifically, you'll want to explain your choice of experimental techniques, defend those choices, and disclose any major limitations. Remember to focus on the data; the experiment is simply a means of producing data that answer your research question. With that in mind, consider the following structure for your paragraph outline:

2.1 Summary Paragraphs: succinctly describe your whole experiment. First, repeat the research question and describe the experimental data you will produce to answer that question. Then, briefly explain each experiment stage—i.e., each of the Methods subsections—stating what was done and why. Finally, list the experiment's main limitations, and describe how, despite the limitations, your experiment adequately answers the research question. After finishing these paragraphs, the reader should understand the basics of your experiment and agree that those methods are appropriate for answering the research question. Your more casual readers will quit the Methods section after these opening paragraphs, but a few readers will delve into the more detailed paragraphs ahead.

2.2 Experiment Stages Sections: elaborate each stage of the experiment—e.g., data, samples, apparatus, procedure, etc.—with its own subsection. For each stage, use your paragraphs to open with a brief summary, defend your choice of experimental technique, elaborate the technique's different components, and transition to the next experiment stage—for example, discussing how the output data of this stage will be used as input data for the next stage. Remember to incorporate any Methods visuals you created in the last chapter. After reading these sections, the reader should thoroughly understand your experiment and support its appropriateness for answering the research question.

2.3 Limitations Section: divulge your experiment's weaknesses. Describe the experiment's main two or three limitations—e.g., assumptions, apparatus shortcomings, data uncertainties, etc. Then make these limitations inconsequential: explain why the experiment, despite its limitations, adequately answers the research question. If divulging weakness makes you feel uneasy, remember that all methods have their flaws; no experiment can explain the whole universe.[67] An article without limitations feels opaque. But disclosing your experiment's weaknesses creates transparency and credibility. You can, however, soften the limitations by discussing them in the middle of the Methods section's story arc—a position of lower emphasis.

2.4 Closing Paragraphs: transition to the Results section. Briefly reiterate the whole experiment. Remind the reader how the experimental output data will yield findings that answer the research question.

3. Results & Discussion

Begin the Results & Discussion by reviewing your figures. In the visualization phase, you created a high-quality chart for each of the experiment's findings. The Results & Discussion section simply explains those charts and uses those explanations to answer your research question.

The Results & Discussion section's main goal is to answer the research question. It does this directly via the main finding. Then, it uses supplementary findings to describe caveats, limitations, and underlying data. Finally, it interprets these findings in the context of the research question. Be sure to separate observations/Results from interpretations/Discussion. With that in mind, consider the following structure for your paragraph outline:

3.1 Opening Paragraphs: tentatively answer the research question. Remind the reader of the research question, summarize the method, and describe how the experiment's output data will answer the research question, generally. Then explain the main finding and hint at its limitations, caveats, and tangents. After finishing these paragraphs, the reader should perceive the main finding and how it answers the research question: this upfront knowledge prepares them for the detailed discussion ahead.

3.2 Findings Sections: elaborate each finding. Each of your main and supplementary findings deserves its own Results & Discussion section. Describe the main finding first; emphasize the main finding by placing it early in the Results & Discussion story arc and indulge your reader by answer the research question upfront.[68] Then describe each supplementary finding, organizing them from broad to narrow: present the big-picture results first, and the nuanced experimental output data last. Title these sections with a short sentence rather than a vague phrase: for example, instead of "Gnomish Cardiovascular Impacts," title the section "Gnomes' pulses and breathing rates quicken." Begin each findings section with objective facts: summarize the finding, explain how any supplementary findings relate to the main finding, and elaborate the finding with additional paragraphs and a figure or table. End each findings section with interpretative Discussion: compare your findings to the literature and apply your findings to answer the research question. If your field assigns Discussion its own section, relocate these discussion points there.

3.3 Conclusion Section: recap the article. The Introduction and Conclusion tell the same story; they describe the same research question, research gap, and broad motivations. The major difference between them: the Introduction tells that story via the literature while the Conclusion tells that story via the Results. Thus, the Conclusion follows the same progression as the Introduction, though in fewer words. Use your paragraphs to 1) reiterate the research question, 2) reiterate the limitations, 3) reiterate the main finding and how it answers the research question, 4) reiterate the supplementary findings, 5) explain the project's application to broader scientific disciplines and research gaps, and 6) explain the project's social benefit by applying the Results to the motivations given in the Introduction's first two paragraphs.

This section-level template sacrifices specific instruction to provide general guidance for developing your paragraph outline. If you want a more definitive guide, see the paragraph-level template ahead.

A Paragraph-level Template

The following template builds on the previous section-level template by elaborating each of its eleven sections with a few paragraphs. For each of these paragraphs, the template gives some guidance to help you develop that paragraph's topic sentence. Note the use of ¶—a symbol called a "pilcrow"—to denote individual paragraphs.

If after reading this template you desire additional instruction, see the appendix in the back of the book for an even more detailed paragraph outline template.

1. Introduction

1.1 Motivation Paragraphs

¶-1 *Broad Motivation:* what broad social problem does your research field contribute to solving?

¶-2 *Specific Research Topic:* how does your niche topic enable your research field to solve that broad problem?

1.2 Background/Literature Review Section

¶-1 *Literature Precedent:* how does the literature address your niche research topic, generally?

¶-2.1* *Weakness Scope:* describe a research area relevant to your topic that exhibits a noteworthy weakness.

¶-2.2* *Weakness References:* cite publications that embody that research area and demonstrate its weakness.

¶-2.3* *Weakness Synthesis:* combine those publications' shortcomings into a unified description of the research area's weakness.

**(Repeat paragraphs 2.1-2.3 for each weakness you wish to reveal in the literature.)*

1.3 Research Question Paragraphs

¶-1 *Research Gap:* how do these weaknesses in the literature combine to reveal a larger research gap?

¶-2 *Research Question:* what question will your project answer to fill that research gap?

1.4 Closing Paragraphs

¶-1 *Additional References:* introduce additional articles you will cite in your Methods or Discussion sections.

¶-2 *Closing:* how will answering your research question fill the research gap and solve the broad motivation?

2. Methods

2.1 Summary Paragraphs

¶-1 *Opening:* how will your experiment produce data that answer the research question?

¶-2 *Overview:* describe each of your experiment's different stages—i.e., each of the Methods subsections.

¶-3 *Limitations:* summarize the limitations, affirm the experiment's ability to answer the research question.

2.2* Experiment Stages Sections

¶-1 *Summarize:* describe the experiment stage and defend your choice of technique.

¶-2 *Elaborate:* multiple paragraphs describing the experimental technique.

¶-3 *Transition:* explain how this experiment stage segues into the next experiment stage.

**(Repeat section 2.2 for each of the experiment's stages, e.g., Data, Samples, Apparatus, Procedure, etc.)*

2.3 Limitations Section

¶-1* *Experiment Limitation:* describe a noteworthy limitation of your experimental method.

**(Repeat paragraph 1 for each of the experiment's limitations)*

¶-2 *Minimize the Limitations:* describe how, despite its limitations, your experiment produces data adequate for answering the research question.

2.4 Closing Paragraphs

¶-1 *Closing:* reiterate the experiment's stages and remind the reader how the experiment's output data answer the research question.

3. Results & Discussion

3.1 Opening Paragraphs

¶-1 *Opening:* foreshadow how the main finding will answer the research question.

3.2* Findings Sections

¶-1 *Summarize:* describe the finding's main point.

¶-2 *Segue to Figure:* introduce the finding's figure and explain how that figure supports the finding.

¶-3 *Elaborate the Figure:* point out any other aspects of the figure—trends, clusters, outliers, intersections, etc.—that add helpful context to the finding.

¶-4 *Interpret the Finding:* interpret the finding into new knowledge relevant to your research question.

¶-5 *Apply the Interpretation:* use your interpretation to answer the research question or to contextualize the main finding.

¶-6 *Broaden the Interpretation:* compare your interpretation with other studies from the literature and apply your interpretation to your broader scientific field.

*(*Repeat section 3.2 for each of the supplementary findings.*)

3.3 Conclusion Section

¶-1 *Reiterate the Project:* broadly, repeat the research question, methods, and main findings.

¶-2 *Reiterate the Limitations:* briefly, repeat the limitations and affirm the Results' ability to answer the research question.

¶-3 *Answer the Research Question:* based on your Results, what is your answer to the research question?

¶-4 *Generalize:* how does that answered research question fill the research gap, and how might that filled research gap advance your broader scientific field?

¶-5 *Motivate:* how does that answered research question solve the motivations described in the article's first paragraph?

A Note on Methods: replication vs. defense

Before we move on, let's acknowledge an important argument about what should be included in the article's most boring section, the Methods. Yes, Methods are boring. Few readers will do more than skim them. Yet Methods underpin our entire project; without them, we are writing opinions, not science.

In light of this scientific importance, the Methods section has two goals. The first goal is mandatory: to convince the reader that we've done proper science using appropriate methods to generate the data that answer our research question. The second is optional: to provide enough information that another researcher could replicate our work.[69]

The argument revolves around whether that second goal—replicability—is optional or mandatory. The problem is the tension between those two goals: convincing the reader of our method's validity requires a short, readable, and honest presentation of what we did and why; but enabling the reader to reproduce our work requires a long, dense, and fractal discussion that covers every experimental caveat. The first style is too short to be comprehensive. The second style is too long to be readable, and it can enable dishonesty by hiding dubious assumptions and poor implementation in the middle of long paragraphs that few will ever read.

It is, therefore, difficult to accomplish both goals in the same Methods section. So what can we do? Luckily, there's a loophole—the Supporting Information, or SI, an appendix to the main text. The SI collects the extra details that most readers don't want to read, including the long-winded, trivial experimental details that a peer might need to replicate our work.

Write your article's Methods section, then, with the first goal in mind—to give the reader enough information to conceptually understand your methods and their limitations so that the reader can deduce your experiment's validity. In addition, include a SI appendix with enough detail for your few closest peers to study your experimental design in case they want to replicate it.

There are two situations, however, where that strategy will fail: 1) if your research field insists on longer, more elaborate Methods and 2) if your project creates a novel experiment design. Again, designing a new experiment is a risky path for your first publication; research is difficult enough without inventing new methods. If you pursue that course, your article becomes more experiment-focused overall; the research gap, research question, results, and conclusions all point to the experimental design, and your Methods must provide enough detail to carry that story.

Whether writing the SI or a long-form, more elaborate version of the Methods section, simply use your experimental procedure and lab notebook to add any information that another researcher would need to replicate your work. Organize the subsections logically—you can follow a similar structure as the short-form Methods. But don't fret too much about readability: few people will fully read the SI or long-form Methods, and the ones who do will endure lengthy writing as long as it's understandable.

And with that, your paragraph outline is complete. Great job so far. You have all of the sections organized. You have paragraph-level details on what you need to write. You have high quality figures for each of your findings. This is really starting to look like a proper research article. The only thing it lacks is more sentences.

WRITE THE FIRST DRAFT: SENTENCES

We've made it to the scary part—putting sentences to paper. But that shouldn't seem so scary now. You've built a robust paragraph-level outline. You have your storytelling tools: give each sentence one main point, start each sentence by emphasizing a known idea, and conclude each sentence with its most important concept. You're letting yourself produce a poorly-written First Draft. All you need to do now is work through each paragraph, consider its topic and other notes, and add some sentences to elaborate.

Adding these sentences isn't difficult. But it becomes difficult when we let cynical voices discourage us. A voice in our head constantly reminds us of our writing's mediocrity. We need to fight that little voice. First, we agree with the voice. It's true, our First Draft is sloppy, disjointed, and poorly written. But we don't need it to be better than that: our goal is to get words on paper. We'll refine those words during the next chapter's editing phase. Second, we indulge the voice. Embrace the bad writing. Write as fast as possible. Unabashedly write bad sentences. Don't use a thesaurus. Don't agonize about the readability. Even sentences without verbs are useful here if they capture an idea that we can edit later on.

Another internal voice undermines our sentence writing: a voice that says we aren't creative enough to write well. That voice is easier to silence, because scientific writing is hardly creative. It's formulaic. We follow common structures and sections. We have books to guide us through the creative aspects of the scientific writing process so we don't have to worry about it. Now, we're probably more creative than we give ourselves credit for. But for stories as straightforward as scientific research, the steps in this book provide plenty of creative guidance for producing an above-average scientific story.

The third voice that inhibits our writing: the criticisms of others. We tend to overblow those potential criticisms, but we can silence them altogether by secluding ourselves. We need not share our low-quality First Draft with anyone. So write it in privacy. The best way is to go incognito. Put on your most non-descript, dark-colored hoodie, go to a coffee shop on the edge of town, sit at a corner table facing the wall, order your coffee under a fake name—nothing that will draw attention; opt for "Bob" instead of "Stephen Hawking" for example—then get cozy and indulge your new alter-ego: do some things you wouldn't normally do, like crank out some bad writing.

WHEN TO MOVE ON

The First Draft represents a huge milestone in your project. It might not be pretty, but it's a complete, written version of your work.

You're done with the First Draft writing phase when:

1. The manuscript lacks any outlining residue: it has no bullet points, numbered hierarchies, or margin notes.

2. Every paragraph is filled with sentences: not just notes or topic ideas.

Maybe your First Draft is barely readable. Maybe it would take your biggest fans a few hours to sort through it and decipher its message. But the content is all there. The writing work is behind you. And you have everything you need for the next chapter where you'll transform the First Draft into a razor-sharp piece of science via some ruthless editing.

But before we move on, let's brace ourselves for the project's final stages. Our project now transitions into an emotionally challenging phase where our precious work gets bombarded with criticism. We've formed a strong bond with our work: it's our project, our writing, our research. Our many months of labor are culminating into a relatively short document. That brevity can feel a bit disheartening—how can so much effort amount to so few words? In this fragile state, we must subject our work to criticism—first from our own edits, and then from our peers' revisions.

Because we identify with our work, that criticism feels personal. Our old perfectionism awakens as we try to define our value by the quality of our journal article. Defensiveness surges through us as we protect that identity from attack.

When our identity, labor, and value depend on this small document, it becomes very difficult to release our perfectionism and tame our defensiveness. But we must. We must moderate our standards and welcome others' suggestions, or this journal article will never reach its potential. We must remember that this publication is not an edifice to ourselves but a contribution to science. It's an offering. And we must share it. And since this research must be shared, the manuscript must evolve into something that our peers can understand. The manuscript's goal isn't our own self-assurance, but interdependent communication and a hope that our small contribution will move science along in directions that reveal new knowledge and help society.

To move forward, then, we must consider this project as no longer ours, but an interdependent scientific collaboration that we had the good fortune to lead. That mindset shift exchanges our perfectionism for pragmatism and our defensiveness for collaboration.

Give your manuscript a rest while you work your way toward that mindset. Take a few days off. Prepare for major edits. Anticipate criticisms. Forget some of the manuscript's intricacies so that you can analyze it with fresh eyes. Then move on to the next chapter where you will edit this poorly-written First Draft into something above-average that your reviewers can work with.

Chapter Recap

In our First Draft, our project finally starts resembling a journal article. We began by selecting our target journal. Then we built the First Draft by adding figures to our project outline, developing that outline into a paragraph-level form, and elaborating that paragraph-level outline with sentences.

First, we discussed some advice from professional writers: give every element one main point, use story arcs, write low-quality first drafts, write every day, and focus on paragraphs as the main component of writing.

Then, we expanded our project outline into a paragraph outline, where each of our article's paragraphs receives a topic sentence and some additional notes. We used three templates to build that paragraph outline—a section-level template, a paragraph-level template, and an extended template in the appendix.

Finally, we added sentences to the paragraph outline: we elaborated each paragraph's topic and notes with actual sentences. To add these sentences successfully, we silenced the cynical voices that inhibit our sentence writing: the voices that say how awful our writing is, how uncreative we are, and how critical our peers will be. By silencing those voices, we empowered ourselves to produce a poorly-written First Draft that contains all the content we need for the editing phase.

See the following page for the writing phase flowchart. See the appendix for a Paragraph Outline template. Download full-sized templates and additional resources from:

www.ProductiveAcademic.com/published

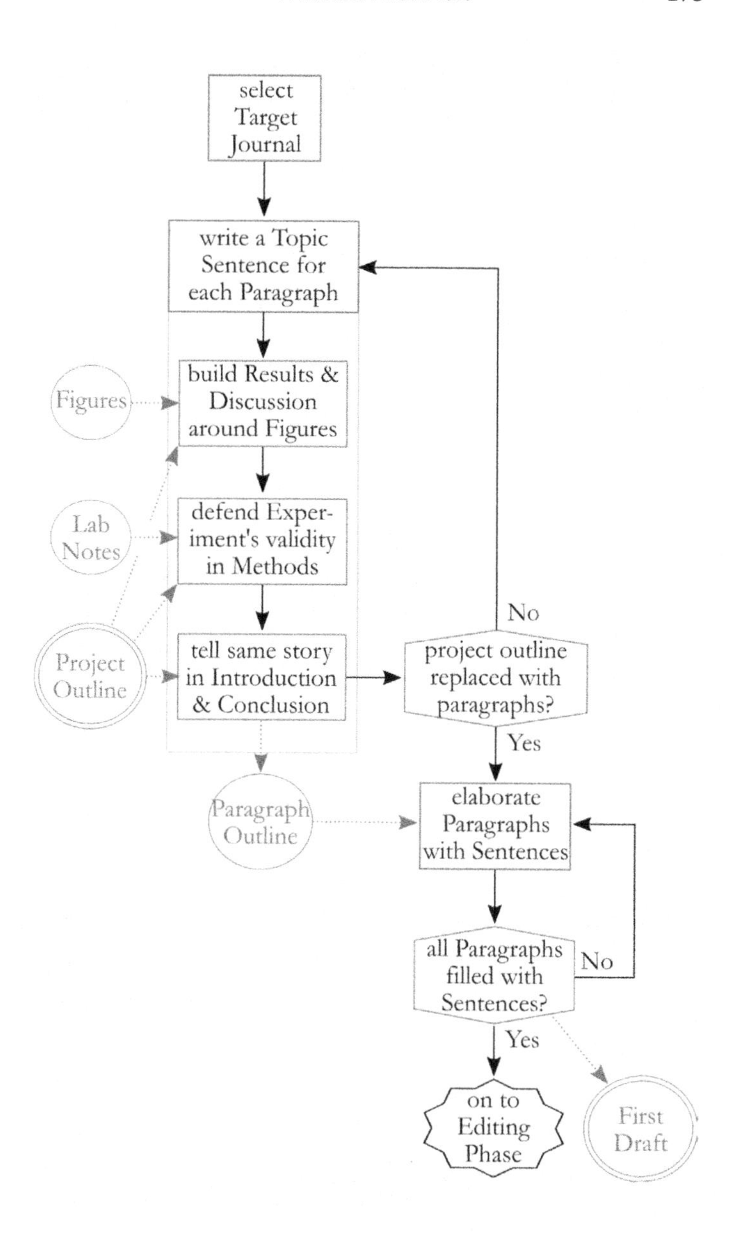
select Target Journal
write a Topic Sentence for each Paragraph
Figures
build Results & Discussion around Figures
Lab Notes
defend Experiment's validity in Methods
Project Outline
tell same story in Introduction & Conclusion
No
project outline replaced with paragraphs?
Yes
Paragraph Outline
elaborate Paragraphs with Sentences
all Paragraphs filled with Sentences?
No
Yes
on to Editing Phase
First Draft

10

Edit into the Second Draft

Perhaps the most embarrassing moment of my first research experience was receiving my supervisor's marked-up version of my early journal article draft. Red ink flooded the manuscript: red arrows pointing out where paragraphs should be moved, entire subsections crossed out in red, and a red list of repeated grammar mistakes. My cheeks turned red to match.

The feedback process itself didn't embarrass me; I expected my supervisor to at least rework the manuscript's style. But I hadn't realized that my supervisor and I expected such different levels of writing quality. I felt exposed by the draft's lack of refinement.

It reminds me of wearing casual attire to a formal conference dinner. Suit and jacket are the norm. So when one shows up underdressed in nice jeans and a button-down shirt, the exposure feels like an awkward spotlight. I mean—not that I've ever done that—I've just heard. From a friend.

Ignorance of my supervisor's expectations led to that underdressed, sub-par draft. But I soon realized another layer of my ignorance: I didn't know how to create a draft that met my supervisor's writing-quality standards. I knew nothing about editing. My editing process involved repeatedly rereading and correcting the entire draft until I thought it flowed well. But even my best attempts with that method would fail the desired standard. I needed a better editing process—something objective, prescriptive, and methodical.

This chapter prescribes such an editing process. Using this process, we will refine our First Draft multiple times: broadly at first, but gradually correcting narrower and narrower details. We will edit our way through story, structure, paragraphs, sentences, and individual words. These edits will refashion our underdressed First Draft into a refined Second Draft that will uphold our work during the vicious revision process in the next chapter. Our project deserves one final push before we send it out into peer-review scrutiny.

THE GOAL OF EDITING

The previous chapter discussed how we stifle our progress when we write and edit at the same time. These tasks require different skills and mindsets, so we must separate them to give our brain a chance to do each task well. Thus, the writing phase produced a poorly-written First Draft. That draft might be barely legible, but it provides a foundation of sentences for us to develop. In the editing phase, we'll take those sentences and ruthlessly prune them into a crisp research story.

Editing cannot, however, perfect our manuscript. For one, we lack the editorial ability; our best writing emerges only after the peer-review process. But more importantly, we don't need to produce a perfect Second Draft. The goal of publishing a journal article is communication. And we can adequately communicate our work without straining to achieve a near-perfect manuscript. Moreover, journal reviewers will find flaws in even the most perfect article: they will never read a manuscript and say, "well, that study is perfect, so let's publish it." No, they need some errors to find and some criticism to give.[70] Let's make their task easier by editing our First Draft work into an imperfect but above-average Second Draft.

We will edit the manuscript in stages. That is, we will read it multiple times and address different problems during each readthrough, starting broadly and then working our way down to narrower details.[71] First, we correct the manuscript's structure, then adjust its paragraphs, and finally edit individual sentences and words. Each readthrough improves our article, making it steadily more readable until we've refined it into our Second Draft.

The Second Draft marks a major turning point in your project. While the First Draft was nowhere near ready for others to look at, the Second Draft is your best solo attempt at writing a journal article. It's the best you can do without peer-review feedback—a process we'll discuss in the next chapter. For now, let's dive into the editing process and polish your manuscript into something good enough to send your reviewers.

EDIT THE STRUCTURE

As you edit each manuscript element—structure, section, paragraph, sentence—remember the storytelling tools from the last chapter. Each of these elements needs one main point and a story arc. Each element must also support the story above it: each sentence elaborates its paragraph, each paragraph embellishes its section, and all elements work toward the single main point of the whole manuscript—the solution of the research question.

In your first editing readthrough, you'll check that the article's overall structure delivers that main story: you'll search the sub-headers, figures, and a few key paragraphs for the story's main features. Your paragraph outline contained those features, but you must verify—after the sentence-writing spree that converted your paragraph outline into your First Draft—that those features remain intact. With that in mind, check the manuscript for the following structural elements:

Consistent Motivation: Do the Introduction and Conclusion discuss the same research gap and motivations? Do they funnel down a similar pattern of broad motivation, wide research field, narrow research topic, and specific research gap?

Consistent Research Question: Do you state the research question at the end of the Introduction, the beginning of the Results, and the beginning of the Conclusion? Do those three statements communicate the same information without being identical?

Answered Research Question: In the Results, do the sub-headers and figures answer the research question? Does the first sub-header describe the main finding, and subsequent sub-headers the supplementary findings? Does the order of those findings flow well given the research question's scope?

Appropriate Methods: Does the Methods section open by describing how the experimental data will answer the research question? Does the Methods section cite appropriate publications to justify its experimental techniques? Do you introduce those citations in the Introduction's background portion? Do the Methods subsections follow a logical progression?

Reword sub-headers, shift their locations, and reorganize paragraphs until you can answer each of those questions affirmatively. Once you can, your manuscript's overall structure will be in good shape: it will show that your project uses appropriate methods to produce findings that answer a research question to fill a research gap and fulfill some broad societal motivation.

EDIT THE SECTIONS

In your next editing readthrough, you'll ask whether each section's smaller story arc has been successfully communicated. In this readthrough you'll focus on each section and the paragraphs within. Remember that paragraphs are the basic component of writing. You want each paragraph to make one point. And you want those points to string together a logical progression that unfolds each section's story.

In this readthrough, your main editing goals are to reorder paragraphs, add paragraphs to provide missing information, and delete paragraphs that distract from the story arc. You want each section's story arc to start broadly, narrow down into specific details, and end broadly by connecting those details back to its main point. That is, each section's opening paragraphs give a forward-looking summary, telling the reader what they are about to read. And each section's closing paragraphs reiterate that summary, reconnect the subsection with the manuscript's main story, or transition to the following section.

To begin, skim the manuscript and underline each paragraph's topic sentence—the sentence that best summarizes the paragraph's main point. If the paragraph makes two points, split the paragraph in two. If the paragraph's main point is unclear, delete the paragraph or replace it with a new paragraph topic sentence describing what the main point ought to be.

You'll reread the underlined paragraph topic sentences—ignoring the other sentences for now—to assess each section's flow. Check each section for the following story arcs:

> Introduction: The story opens with a broad motivation, narrows down to a research topic, gives background information for that topic, develops the research gap, introduces the research question, and closes with a paragraph that reminds readers how the research question connects to the research field and motivation.
>
> Methods: The story opens by focusing on data: what data will answer the research question, and what experiments will create that data? Then, it summarizes the subsections—the different stages of the experiment—and describes the limitations. Each subsection opens by summarizing the technique and explaining why that technique is appropriate for this particular research problem. Subsequent paragraphs elaborate the technique and the closing paragraphs transition to the next subsection. The Methods concludes by disclosing the

limitations, reassuring that they do not undermine the experiment, and then reiterating how the experiment's output data address the research question.

Results & Discussion: The story opens by reiterating the research question and foreshadowing the main finding. Each subsection opens by summarizing the finding, then providing the data and figures that elaborate the finding, then interpreting the finding in terms of the literature and research question.

Conclusion: The story reiterates the research question, limitations, results, and conclusions, and then synthesizes that information into something more general—something that applies to the larger research field. It closes by connecting those generalizations back to the Introduction's broad motivations.

Rewrite paragraph topic sentences, relocate paragraphs, and delete or create paragraphs to tighten those story arcs until you can check off each item in that list. Once you can, each section's story will be in good shape: it will follow a pattern that reads well and covers your project's main themes.

So far so good. Thanks to diligent outlining, your structure and section readthroughs likely required only minor edits. The following readthroughs, however, which refine your First Draft's mediocre writing, will take more work. Take a deep breath. Follow the instructions. And take it step by step.

EDIT THE PARAGRAPHS

Like the other elements of writing, each paragraph tells its own story. In this readthrough, you'll focus on each paragraph and the sentences within. You want each sentence to make a clear point, and you want that point to contribute to the paragraph's story. Ignore the particular words in each sentence for now—you don't need a thesaurus quite yet. Rather, note the underlined topic sentence for each paragraph and ensure that the paragraph's other sentences follow that theme.

There are many ways to write a paragraph, but to keep it simple we'll focus on two paragraph types: "point-first" and "point-last".[72] The point-first type is our go-to paragraph; it makes up 75% of what we write. Its main goal is to add description to existing ideas, and it does so by following a simple story structure. It opens with its topic sentence, occasionally placing a transition sentence before it. Then the other sentences simply describe that topic in greater detail. The paragraph you are now reading, for example, illustrates this type of structure; it opens with its topic—the point-first paragraph type—followed by more sentences that elaborate the paragraph type with description and an example.

The point-last paragraph type is used less frequently, and only to shift the story in a new direction or introduce a new idea. We open these paragraphs by foreshadowing the main idea, but the paragraph's true topic only emerges in its final sentence. The final sentence describes the new idea or shifts the story, and it uses all of the preceding sentences to guide the reader there. Each sentence must do more than support the main point, it must provide movement. The start of each sentence should begin with a known idea and then move toward a new idea. That new idea should start the next sentence and help it introduce a subsequent new idea until the reader has traversed enough information to grasp the paragraph's topic in the closing sentence. The paragraph you are about to read provides an example of this point-last paragraph type.

Though the structural differences between these two paragraph types have practical importance, we can also use their differences to leverage the way our reader's brain processes information. As we read, we fall into rhythms. Those rhythms develop an almost lyrical nature that lulls our brain into a reading cadence. In this cadence, we process information easily because each new piece of information follows a similar form as the last. But this cadence makes it difficult for the author to emphasize when new information is particularly important. To emphasize new information, we must break this cadence. We break it by jarring our reader with a new writing pattern. We shorten our sentences. We use an uncommon paragraph type. We change something about the rhythm, and the reader notices. The change signals their brain—what you are reading now is different than what you were reading before—and it heightens the reader's attention. Even in isolation, the point-last paragraph type has value because its structure promotes a specific narrative style. But its greater value comes from the context of its neighboring paragraphs—from its ability to break from the point-first paragraph type, which abruptly changes the writing pattern to emphasize an important topic.

To summarize, the point-first paragraph type is efficient. Its internal structure provides a rhythm that effectively communicates its main point. Clusters of point-first paragraphs provide a cadence that plows through information.

The point-last paragraph type is emphatic. Its internal structure emphasizes the last sentence. Breaking a cluster of point-first paragraphs with a point-last paragraph changes the writing pattern and lends the paragraph greater prominence.

Use the point-first paragraph type to deliver supporting information. Use the point-last paragraph type to emphasize important points. Now, read through the manuscript, decide each paragraph's type, and reorganize each paragraph's sentences accordingly:

1. Revisit each paragraph's underlined topic sentence. Circle any paragraphs that shift the story in a new direction, introduce a new idea, or add emphasis: many section's opening and closing paragraphs will fit that description. These circled paragraphs should be point-last paragraphs. You can assume that the non-circled paragraphs—probably about three-quarters of the manuscript—will be of the point-first paragraph type.

2. Look through all of the point-first paragraphs. Each of them should have their topic sentence somewhere near the beginning of the paragraph—often the first sentence. Every subsequent sentence should elaborate that topic with smaller details. Address any off-topic sentences by deleting them, moving them to an on-topic paragraph, or using them as the topic sentence of a new paragraph.

3. Look through all of the point-last paragraphs—the ones you circled. Their topic sentence should be near the end of the paragraph. Their opening sentence should hint at the topic. Each subsequent sentence does one of two things. It starts with a known idea and

introduces a new idea that leads into the next sentence. Or it elaborates the previous sentence and hints at the paragraph's topic. You must edit your sentences to achieve one of those tasks. These point-last paragraphs require greater editing effort, but getting them right feels quite satisfying.

Finally, if you're interested in refining the writing style even more, revisit the paragraphs and focus on their length. Most of your manuscript should comprise clusters of medium-length point-first paragraphs to create a strong, underlying cadence. When you desire to break that cadence, adjusting the paragraph lengths can help.

Start with the circled paragraphs and decide whether you want them to add emphasis or to quickly move the story along. Shorten the emphasis-giving paragraphs—make them as succinct as possible. That brevity breaks the reading cadence even more strongly, which gives the paragraphs extra emphasis.

For the other circled paragraphs—the ones that quickly move the story along—lengthen them. Their structural change still signals a cadence shift to the reader, but greater length reduces their emphasis and gives you more room to communicate the many ideas needed to move your story along.

And among these short, medium, and long paragraphs, you'll want additional variety in length to make the reading more interesting. A string of identical-length medium paragraphs makes for boring reading. But subtle variations in length—from medium-short to medium-long—makes them more interesting without breaking their cadence.

EDIT THE SENTENCES

With the structure, sections, and paragraphs in order, let us now battle our long-time nemesis—the sentence. But this battle will be different than our past struggles. We lost our past battles because of bad writing habits—binge writing, simultaneous writing-editing, using sentences as writing's main component. But we're above that nonsense now. We are reborn writing phoenixes, rising from our bad-writing ashes, blazing forth into eloquence. Or we're at least producing above-average writing without stressing about it.

In this readthrough, you'll look at each sentence and focus on the words within. First, begin and end each sentence strategically. Remember that sentences, although short, still follow a story arc. A sentence starts with known information, adds context in the middle, and ends on a point of emphasis. Organize each sentence to leverage that structure. That is, avoid starting or ending sentences with unimportant phrases; put those phrases in the sentence's middle. Then, start sentences with their subjects and end them with their main point.

Second, use appropriate verb types.[73] Active verbs—where the subject performs the action—empower your sentences. They also shorten them, which makes your writing more succinct. Those traits benefit scientific writing, so you should favor active verbs. But you shouldn't always use them. Suppose you want to emphasize an idea. If active voice forces that idea to the sentence's middle, it deemphasizes it. Rather, start the sentence with that idea and use whatever verb form accommodates that structure. Consider, for example, the sentence "The potion accelerated the gnome's pulse—an unexpected side effect." If you want to emphasize the gnomes rather than the potion, you might rewrite that sentence without an active verb as "The gnome's pulse was accelerated by the potion—an unexpected side effect."

Finally, vary the sentence length. Like paragraphs, most sentences should have a medium length to promote a helpful cadence. But we can break that cadence strategically. Short sentences, for example, halt the reader. They demand attention. Use short sentences to describe powerful ideas.[74] Break complex concepts into short sentences. Then deliver those short sentences one after another to compile the larger concept. Unfortunately—as illustrated by this sentence here—we often do the opposite: we explain our most difficult material using long sentences—maybe because we believe that their many interrelated clauses give us more opportunity to intricately connect various pieces of information, or that their length commands some sort of attention—but long sentences are too wordy to effectively communicate new and sophisticated concepts. Long sentences are best used to rush our writing through a series of familiar ideas.

We can easily stress over sentence editing if we try to make each sentence perfect. But by focusing on story arcs, appropriate verb types, and sentence length, we greatly improve our writing without agonizing over every detail. With that in mind, edit your sentences using the following checklist:

1. Read through each sentence and identify its two most important phrases. These are usually nouns. Move them to the beginning and end of the sentence, reserving the beginning for the sentence's subject and the end for its most important phrase.

2. Read through every sentence and choose the verb type that accommodates the sentences beginning/ending phrases. Lean toward active verbs, but use the others to prioritize intentional word orderings.

3. When in doubt, put the subject and verb at the beginning of the sentence and keep them together. Creative, literary fiction seethes of complicated sentences that buck this rule. But in technical writing, where your greatest aim is clarity, a subject-verb beginning never hurts.

4. If a sentence doesn't have a subject and verb, it's not a sentence, it's a fragment. We don't use fragments in technical writing. Only poets do. For emphasis. For art. For confusion?

5. Read through the manuscript and underline sentences that make important points or that explain complicated details. Shorten these sentences. Reword them. Rewrite them as multiple short sentences instead of a few long ones.

6. Read through the manuscript and draw a box around any droning parts with numerous medium-length sentences, or any parts with lots of basic information. Consider reworking those parts into longer sentences to add some variety and cover basic information more quickly.

7. Read through the manuscript and note any parts with multiple long-length sentences or multiple short-length

sentences in a row. Unless these sequences are intentional—to quicken the story, add emphasis, or explain complexity—consider reworking them into medium-length sentences.

EDIT THE WORDS

Great work so far—your Second Draft is really blossoming. The individual sentences read well. They combine into meaningful paragraphs that produce strategic cadences, build section-level story arcs, and emphasize the journal article's main points. But there are still some mistakes below the sentence level that you must deal with. You must improve your choices of individual words.

Of course, you've been editing words all along. But until now, those edits have been in the context of structure, paragraphs, and sentences. Now you must isolate those words; you must critique your word choices independent of their role in the sentence. That is, some words—regardless of where they appear in the sentence structure—are wrong. You must fix them.

For this final task, you'll search the manuscript for a specific error, fix it, and repeat. Though no single fix will revitalize your writing, each error you correct will marginally improve the manuscript.

The list below corrects many common mistakes you'll find in academic writing.[75] It's a long list: work through as many corrections as you can endure, focus on your most pervasive errors, and you'll slowly improve the manuscript's brevity and readability. Now's your chance to get out that thesaurus.

Weak Verbs: Search for the following words: change, affect, occur, facilitate, perform, conduct, implement, and similar verbs that are weak and ambiguous. Replace them with stronger alternatives like: modify, create, increase, decrease, invade, react, inhibit, accelerate, and disrupt.[76]

Nominalizations: When we turn verbs into nouns, we often suppress a strong verb as the false subject of a sentence. For example, "Increasing toxicity is caused by X." becomes, "X increases toxicity." Search for words ending in -ence, -ent, -ion, -ize to find some nominalizations, then turn them back into verbs.[77]

Adverbs: Adverbs modify verbs and adjectives. They add nuance to literary writing, but we academic writers often use them to inflate our claims, with words like: substantially, rarely, or negligibly. These types of words lack substance, and we have better methods for creating emphasis. Adverbs have little use in academic writing.[78] Keep some if you must but try to eliminate the majority. To find most adverbs, search for words ending in -ly. For adverbs that subtly change a word's meaning, find a better word: e.g., "increasingly slowed" becomes "decelerated." For adverbs that repeat meaning already contained in a word, remove them: e.g., "violently explode" becomes "explode."

Verb Qualifiers: Search for verb qualifiers like: sort of, tend to, seem to, could have, begin to, etc. and remove them.[79] If you're using these qualifiers to hedge a claim, reframe that claim into something more defensible.

Jargon: Favor simple words over complicated ones. For the reader's sake, avoid jargon unless it provides clear benefits for making the writing more succinct. If you must use jargon, place it in the middle of sentences where it draws the least emphasis.

Acronyms: A type of jargon, avoid acronyms unless they are commonly known or provide clear benefits for making your writing more succinct. It's annoying to continually consult the nomenclature table of an acronym-heavy publication. Consider removing all acronyms, unless your manuscript uses them more than four times. Otherwise, they won't add much brevity, but might alienate your readers.

Abbreviations: Abbreviations can be more useful than acronyms because they have a stronger ability to retain their original meaning in their shortened form. Make them unambiguous. Don't use "Scenario A" when "Mild Scenario" will do.

Em Dash (—): Em dashes—long dashes the width of a capital M—have a variety of uses. Mainly, they help us go on short tangents. They can be used in the middle of a sentence—often instead of parentheses—or at the end of a sentence where you might want to place an incomplete thought in the sentence's most powerful position—like this.

Colon (:): Colons have a few nuanced uses, but you should mainly use them to introduce a list at the end of a sentence. Search for colons, if they don't introduce a list, they can probably be replaced with an em dash.

Semicolon (;): Semicolons connect two independent clauses to balance them against each other. Semicolons can be useful, but are complicated to get right. Grammatically, they can be replaced with periods, which changes the writing's emphasis but not its meaning. Avoid semicolons if you don't want to deal with them.

Exclamation Point (!): Exclamation points are used when a person's actual quotation was an exclamation. In academic writing, they come off as silly attempts at emphasis. Avoid them.

However & For Example: These phrases belong in the middle of sentences, not at the beginning. Place them at a natural pivot point and bookend them with commas. This sentence, for example, illustrates the phrase's correct placement.

But & Yet: These words belong at the beginning of a sentence. But they are too casual for academic writing.

Not & No: Readers overlook these small words too easily, and then fail to realize that you intended something negative instead of positive. Replace these words with negative verbs and expressions, e.g., "not accurate" becomes "inaccurate."

Because: Many phrases—e.g., due to, as a consequence of, due to the fact that, etc.—should be replaced with "because."

To: Many phrases—e.g., in an effort to, in order to, etc.—should be replaced with "to."

In this study: Unless you are distinguishing your study from other publications—e.g., in comparison to other literature—it is implied that your writing always refers to your own article. Thus, the phrase "in this study" can usually be removed.

Its & It's: "It's" is a contraction that means "it is". "Its" is a possessive pronoun indicating that something belongs to "it". Search for these and fix them as needed.

This, It, That, & These: By themselves, these words can be ambiguous. Search for them in your manuscript. If their meaning is clear—i.e., it is obvious what noun they represent—then keep them. Otherwise, follow them with a noun that clarifies their meaning.

While: "While" should only be used if you can replace it with "during the time that" without changing its meaning. If contrasting two ideas, use "although" instead. If used in the middle of a sentence followed by a comma, replace it with "but" or "and." Otherwise, delete it.[80]

Of: Search for prepositional phrases that use "of" and reorder them so that the "of" is unnecessary. E.g., "method of delivery" becomes "delivery method."

Data: Data is a plural noun. Give it a plural verb. E.g., "The data shows" becomes "The data show".

Effect: A noun which means "result"—so don't use it as a verb. In fact, don't use "affect" as a verb either—you can think of stronger alternatives.[81]

That & Which: "That" indicates the noun that you are referring to. "Which" elaborates the noun, which adds some superfluous detail. If you remove a which-phrase from a sentence, its meaning doesn't change, it just loses some detail. The common error is to use "which" instead of "that". Search for every "which." If the "which" elaborates a noun, try to rephrase the sentence to remove the "which." Otherwise, delete the "which" or replace it with "that" if appropriate.

Comparisons: "Better," "worse," and other comparisons must include the thing you are comparing against. Something cannot be merely better; it must be better than something else.

Prepositional Phrases: Search for the following words: by, of, to, for, toward, on, at, from, in, with, as. These words—especially clusters of them—often signal unnecessary phrases. Consider reworking your sentences to remove the need for these prepositional phrases.[82]

And & Or: Search for "and" and "or" to see if they form two-word lists—or dyads.[83] Many dyads, especially in the same sentence, dull your writing—for example: a sentence or phrase with four or five dyads feels rhythmic and droning, which lulls and bores your tired and confused readers. If appropriate, opt for one noun instead of a list of two or more.

Work through the edits in that list. Edit individual words until it's unbearable.[84] Then stop. Congratulations—you're done with editing and nearly done with the Second Draft. All that remains is the title and abstract.

WRITE THE TITLE AND ABSTRACT

Yes, if you hadn't noticed, you've come all this way without writing a title or abstract. It's best to save these for last. Partly because they're easier to write at the end: these two elements summarize your entire article, so it's helpful to know what the complete manuscript actually says before you write them.

The title and abstract also serve a different purpose than the main IMRaD body, and they benefit from a different writing mindset. At this point, you've completed your journal article: a manuscript without a title and abstract still tells a complete story.

Then what do the title and abstract accomplish? Marketing. The title and abstract hook potential readers to download your publication. Once they've downloaded it, the quality of the IMRaD content will dictate whether the reader cites your work. But for anyone to read your publication in the first place, they must download it, and you must persuade them to download it with your title and abstract.

Consider, for example, how you browsed publications during your literature review. You skimmed hundreds of articles, made snap judgements about what you read, and based those judgements on the articles' titles and abstracts. You probably overlooked many useful publications because their titles and abstracts didn't send a strong enough signal or because they failed to appear in your search engine results altogether. So if you feel strongly that your journal article advances science—that it deserves to be read—then you must craft a persuasive title and abstract so that your peers don't overlook your helpful contribution.

Key Words

Both title and abstract begin with a list of key words. Key words are a set of phrases describing the different research niches related to your article. Sometimes publications are tagged with an actual list of key words. These directly influence how search engines find those articles. Other times, key words are less obvious, but creating a list of them now, and working that list into your title and abstract will improve your article's search results.

Let's discuss a few strategies for building a list of key words. Start by scanning your manuscript for common phrases. These phrases might describe the research topic, experimental methods, results, or other components of the project. Focus on your research question, research gap, and conclusion and identify their most important phrases.

Then, search your referenced articles for common key words—especially the exemplary articles that you cite most often. Add these publications' key words to your list. Scan their titles and abstracts for words that describe the research discipline, related fields, important topics, or other phrases relevant to your project.

Also, consider your readers' viewpoint. What questions are they asking that your publication can answer? What phrases will they search for during their literature review? Add those phrases to the key words list.

Your list may quickly balloon to dozens of key words, but you need only keep six or seven. You can start filtering that list by entering each key word into a search engine to see what publications it finds.[85] If a key word search produces many relevant journal articles, keep it in your list.

After removing any key words with poor search results, organize the remaining key words in order of importance: place the strongest key word at the top, the next strongest key word below it, and so on. You will work the top six or seven key words into your abstract and the top two or three into the title.

Title

A good title contains your strongest key words and communicates your article's main story—all in just 10-15 words. You can achieve this by writing a very long title, then trimming it down.[86] Start by combining your top three key words, your research question, a one-sentence summary of your research gap, a one sentence-summary of your method, and your main finding into one very long title. Then make it shorter. First, delete any words that can be removed without changing the title's meaning. Then, delete any words that distract from your project's most important point. Once you've trimmed the title down to fewer than 15 words, reorganize it to highlight the main finding. If possible, describe the main finding using an active verb.

One effective format is the "Main Title: Subtitle" approach. In this case, the main title is short. It grabs the reader's attention with the most important topic, key word, or research niche. The subtitle is longer and reads more like a newspaper headline. It shows the reader your main finding and hints at the research question. It helps if the subtitle is a complete sentence—albeit a short one—because the right verb can go a long way in communicating your research question and main finding.

Whatever format you use, stay on point. Avoid sweeping, catch-all titles—they are too ambiguous to hook readers. Avoid jargon, buzz words, or pump-up words—they dilute the project's main point. Focus on key words, the research question, and the main finding that answers it.

Let's revisit our potions-making friend for an example of how to create a title. Suppose she begins with:

Key Words: Trait-reversal, Fur-infusion, Productivity

Research Question: Can a trait-reversal fur-infusion create a productivity potion? Or, more generally, can trait-reversal be achieved by fur-infusion potions?

Research Gap: Lack of data on trait-reversal potions, especially in the fur-infusion field.

Research Method: testing fur-infusion potions made from vinegar and lemon juice solvents with cat, opossum, and sloth hairs on garden gnomes.

Main Finding: under the influence of a vinegar-sloth-hair fur-infusion potion, the gnomes busily weeded their garden and repaired a broken wall.

Our friend is tempted to use a sweeping title like, "On Trait-reversal Fur-infusions." This sort of title makes the project feel substantial, but potential readers won't discern the research question or the main finding. She needs something more on-point.

Alternatively, she starts with a long title, "We test vinegar and lemon juice plus cat, opossum, and sloth hair to produce a trait-reversal fur-infusion that causes garden gnomes to become more productive, evidenced by them weeding their garden and repairing a wall, which provides helpful data for the nascent trait-reversal field." This title is clearly too long, but it's a starting point for creating something shorter.

First she finds words that can be deleted without changing the title's meaning. She replaces "We test vinegar and lemon juice plus cat, opossum, and sloth hair" with just "vinegar-sloth-hair" because it feels too specific and her other potions combinations created inconclusive findings. She shortens the part about weeding and wall repair. And she removes the last part about the trait-reversal field: she figures including the "trait-reversal," "fur-infusion," and "productivity" key words will be enough to point to the research gap. This leaves her with: "Vinegar-sloth-hair trait-reversal fur-infusion causes garden gnomes to become productive and weed their garden."

That title's okay—it's short enough and contains everything she needs, but its first words emphasize "Vinegar-sloth-hair" and our friend really wants to emphasize the research gap. Using the Main Title: Subtitle approach, she comes up with, "Productivity via trait-reversal fur-infusion: vinegar and sloth hair transform lazy gnomes into industrious gardeners." This title leads with the research gap and question, it hints at the method—vinegar and sloth hair tested on gnomes—and summarizes the main finding—industrious gardeners.

Abstract

The abstract is a bit easier to write than the title because it's longer—around 150-250 words. It has three main goals:

1. The abstract's first goal is to summarize your article's entire story by covering each IMRaD section's highlights. At a minimum, this means the research question, the research method, main finding, and main conclusion.

2. Additionally, since the abstract influences search engine results, you'll want to fill it with your strongest six or seven key words.

3. And since the abstract and title market your article together, their content must be strongly connected. The abstract should expand on anything hinted at in the title.

The easiest way to begin the abstract is to compile your manuscript's best sentences and rework them into a cohesive paragraph.[87] Read through the manuscript, copy the best sentence that describes the motivation, research question, each method subsection, each finding, and the main conclusion. Once you string those sentences together, you'll have the abstract's content. But you must rewrite it to improve the flow and reduce its length.

The abstract uses a story structure similar to the Introduction, except that it tightens its scope more abruptly. It narrows from motivation to research question in two sentences, spends a few more sentences describing the project, and then broadens from conclusion to motivation. The following framework gives an example:

"To address [broader research motivation], we study [narrow niche topic]. Our research question asks [your research question or hypothesis here]. We answer this

> research question by using [high level sentence about Methods] to produce [most important output data]. Specifically, we [use sub-method 1, apply sub-method 2, and calculate sub-method 3 to produce output 1 and output 2]. This output shows that [supplementary finding 1] and that [supplementary finding 2]. More significantly, the experimental data show that [main finding]. Based on this result, we conclude that [main conclusion and the answer to the research question]. This conclusion suggests that [main application or interpretation for the broad research field], which contributes to solving [research gap] and improving [broad research motivation]."

If that abstract format feels blunt, remember that this isn't literary fiction. Clarity outweighs style—especially in the word-constrained abstract. Use the words "research question," "method," "result," and "conclusion" to indicate those topics. It may feel terse, but the reader will know exactly what you intend. So start with the example above and fill in the blanks using the sentences you plucked from the manuscript. Then modify the sentences to highlight key words, synchronize with the title, and tell the project's whole story.

TIPS FOR SUCCESSFUL EDITING

Although writing was a fast-paced effort to get thoughts onto paper, editing is a methodical exercise that requires an unbiased, critical eye. Editing is a bit more painful than writing: it moves slowly, requires multiple rereads, and rarely feels serendipitous. Luckily, editing is also more prescriptive: only *you* can write your manuscript's First Draft, but any editor can refine it into a high-quality Second Draft. To succeed in editing, you must exchange your author persona for the role of unbiased editor. Below are a few tips to help you do that:

Have a refiner's mindset. Remember that you intentionally produced a poorly-written First Draft. It must be refined—in the true sense of the word. Your First Draft is an ore filled with gold, but it's mostly rock. It needs crushing, heating, and pressure to separate the precious from the mundane. Be ruthless and purge the First Draft of its impurities.

Read the draft out loud. This helps you disconnect a bit from your authorship and edit the manuscript with less bias. Reading out loud also helps you find mistakes that your mental reading overlooks. You can skim a bad sentence when reading in your head, but your tongue will stumble over its awkwardness.

Take it slow. Edit the manuscript in batches. Leave yourself useful editorial notes. And since editing is one of the few research tasks we can accomplish efficiently with paper and pen, print out the manuscript, grab a red pen, and work on it in a pleasant environment—all of these will help to slow your editing down.

WHEN TO MOVE ON

You'll reread the manuscript many times during editing. Every editing readthrough improves the article, but each of those readthroughs have diminishing returns; your first edit corrects many more issues than your tenth edit does. Still, it's difficult to know when to stop.

At this stage in the research process, your manuscript need only be good enough to share with your supervisor. You'll pursue a higher standard for your Final Draft—the one that gets published. But since the Second Draft will absorb suggestions from many different reviewers, and whole paragraphs and even subsections might change, it need not be of journal-submission quality. You must rather seek balance—a manuscript good enough for reviewers to easily read, but not so good that you spend unnecessary time improving it.

That standard is a bit vague, so see the following criteria for something more specific. You're done with the Second Draft edits when you finish the following readthroughs:

1. Check the broad structure. Read the title, abstract, and Introduction. Read the Methods opening paragraphs and sub-headers. Read the Results sub-headers, each figure, and the Conclusion. Did this short readthrough deliver the article's main story—minus some smaller details?

2. Check the paragraph flow. Skim the manuscript from start to finish. Read the first and last sentence of each paragraph, unless that paragraph opens or concludes a subsection—then read the whole thing. This readthrough skims the majority of your paragraph's topic sentences. It checks the manuscript's topical flow. Do the transitions between paragraphs make sense? Does each paragraph move the story in the correct direction?

3. Check the readability. Read the entire manuscript out loud. This readthrough checks for awkward grammar or other failures. You should be able to complete the readthrough without major verbal stumbles. Are there spots where you stumble over your words? Are there sentences with unclear meaning?

Now take a moment and celebrate. You've worked through a lot to get to this point. You have a crisp Second Draft with a cohesive story that contributes to broader science. You could submit it to a journal now and it would likely get past the editor to some actual reviewers. And that is quite a feat.

In the next section, however, your celebration will end as you open your project to criticism. Your coauthors will fill the manuscript with red ink. Journal reviewers will reveal the work's many flaws.

But it's time to send your young manuscript out into the world. And even though the real world might be harsh, the criticism will mature your article into something worthy of publication: something that will make its parents proud—or at least relieved that it's finally moving out of the house.

Chapter Recap

Editing turns our First Draft into a crisp Second Draft that is ready for the revision process. Over multiple readthroughs, we first checked our manuscript's structure for the correct content and its sections for good paragraph flow.

Next, we edited our paragraphs. We gave each paragraph one main point. We discussed two paragraph types and used them to create a cadence that promotes efficient reading or to break that cadence for emphasis. We also varied paragraph length to manipulate cadence and improve style.

Then, we edited sentences. We gave sentences one main point, began and ended them with important ideas, and varied their lengths to manipulate reading cadence. We favored active verbs, but used other verbs if they supported the strategic placement of a sentence's beginning and ending phrases.

Finally, we completed the editing process by hunting for common word choice errors. The chapter provides a long list of these common errors with guidelines for correcting them.

After completing our edits, we wrote the title and abstract, which market our manuscript to potential readers. We built them from a list of key words. The title describes our project's most important takeaways. The abstract elaborates the title and summarizes the whole article—including its research question, method, main finding, and main conclusion.

See the following page for the editing phase flowchart. Download additional resources, including a printable version of this chapter's word editing list from:

www.ProductiveAcademic.com/published

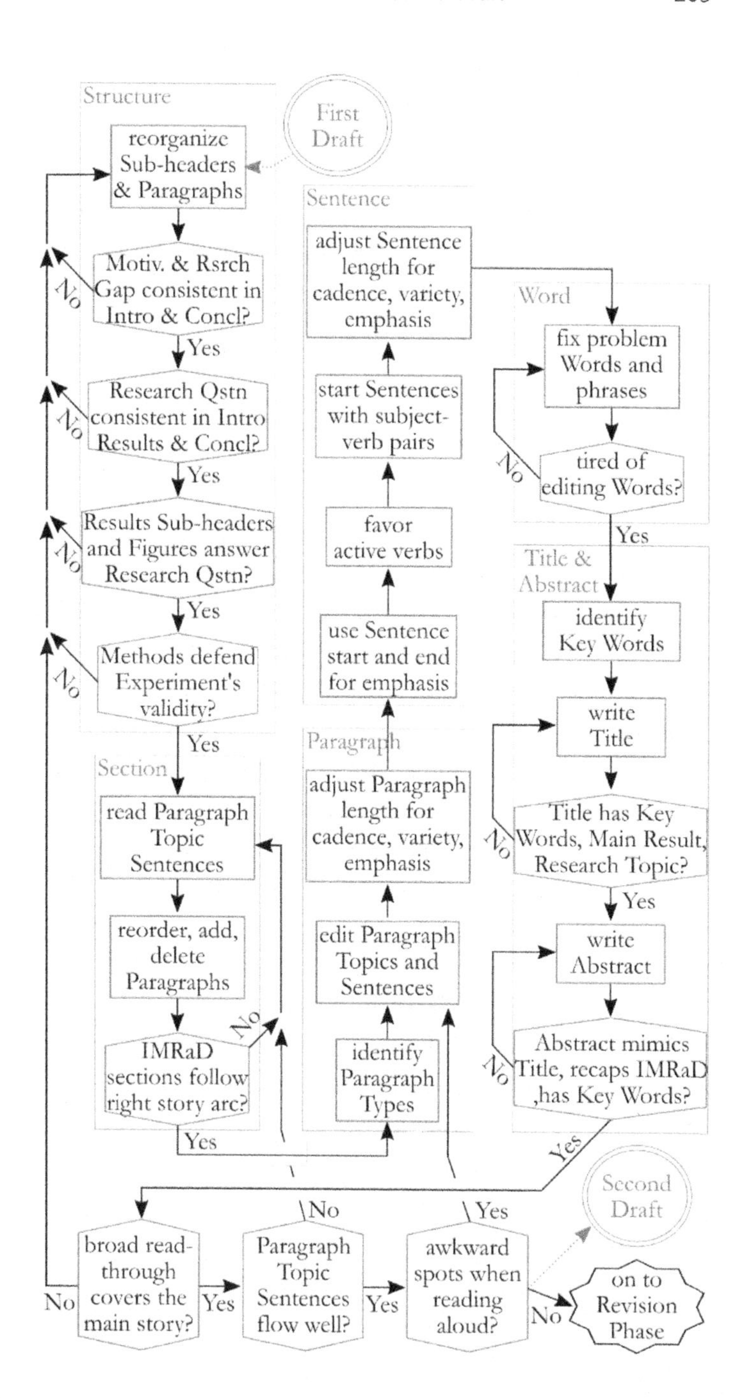
Structure
First Draft
reorganize Sub-headers & Paragraphs
Motiv. & Rsrch Gap consistent in Intro & Concl?
No
Yes
Research Qstn consistent in Intro Results & Concl?
No
Yes
Results Sub-headers and Figures answer Research Qstn?
No
Yes
Methods defend Experiment's validity?
No
Yes
Section
read Paragraph Topic Sentences
reorder, add, delete Paragraphs
IMRaD sections follow right story arc?
No
Yes
Sentence
adjust Sentence length for cadence, variety, emphasis
start Sentences with subject-verb pairs
favor active verbs
use Sentence start and end for emphasis
Paragraph
adjust Paragraph length for cadence, variety, emphasis
edit Paragraph Topics and Sentences
identify Paragraph Types
Word
fix problem Words and phrases
tired of editing Words?
No
Yes
Title & Abstract
identify Key Words
write Title
Title has Key Words, Main Result, Research Topic?
No
Yes
write Abstract
Abstract mimics Title, recaps IMRaD ,has Key Words?
No
Yes
Second Draft
broad read-through covers the main story?
No
Yes
Paragraph Topic Sentences flow well?
No
Yes
awkward spots when reading aloud?
Yes
No
on to Revision Phase

11

Revise until Published

Revising my manuscript for the third—yes, third—round of peer review felt like playing extra innings in little league baseball. Ten-year-old me found baseball amusing at best. I liked playing catch. I enjoyed eating sunflower seeds. But the actual games involved a bunch of kids—half of whom (myself included) could barely throw, catch, or hit a baseball—attempting inning after inning of clown-like athleticism. It's excruciating! And if the two teams have the same score after nine of these sloppy innings, they play extra innings. After a few extra innings, I'm tired of playing catch, I've eaten my sunflower seeds, and I hardly care if my team wins or loses. I want to go home, play with Legos, and try baseball again some other day.

Peer review—especially three rounds of it—can be equally excruciating. By the end, I cynically doubted if half of my reviewers were capable of writing, researching, or editing their own work, let alone commenting on mine. I was tired of fighting over trivial issues. I hardly cared anymore if I published in this journal. I just wanted to go home, play with Legos, and try a different journal some other day.

That revision felt slow, random, even combative, but the real problem was my defensive attitude. It's tough submitting my work to criticism. I feel like I'm letting strangers undermine my masterpiece.

But we must release those sentiments to conquer the revision process. We must admit that our best individual efforts fail the journal's publication standards. We must believe that reviewers want our work to succeed. And we must approach the process dispassionately so that we can strategically manage reviewer comments and push our manuscript past those gatekeepers to publication.

This chapter concludes your publication journey by navigating the emotional and practical hurdles of the revision process. It addresses the difficulty of subjecting your work to scrutiny. It gives a roadmap for the internal-review and journal-review processes. And it develops strategies for handling different kinds of peer-review comments. In the end, you'll have a battered but refined final manuscript. It won't quite feel like "yours" anymore, but it will gain the approval of your peers. It's time to muster one final effort to maneuver your project through the reviewal process and get it, finally, published.

THE GOAL OF REVISION

The previous chapter produced a Second Draft—a version of your work that you feel confident enough about to share with your supervisor. This Second Draft is good, but it is not good enough for publication—both for noble and practical reasons.

The noble reason—we want to produce quality work that advances scientific knowledge. This means our work must be readable, sensible, novel, logical, and lots of other adjectives that describe high-quality scientific research. If we're honest, that level of quality exceeds our capabilities. Not just because we are still developing our research and writing skills, but because we don't have the ability to read our work from another person's perspective and wholly understand how well our readers will receive it. We need reviewers' feedback to create a manuscript that communicates with and appeals to our readers.

The practical reason that our Second Draft is not ready for publication—scientific publishing has gatekeepers, and they will not let us advance without completing the peer-review process. Even if we don't like the idea of feedback, we have little choice if we want to publish a peer-reviewed article. "Peer-reviewed" is synonymous with "vetted by the scientific community," which is synonymous with "quality."

Certainly, the revision process isn't perfect. In our literature review, we discovered many mediocre articles that somehow squeezed through the peer-review process. We'll also meet many reviewers who seem to have vendettas against us. But most reviewers are competent and have the noble reason—advancing scientific knowledge—at heart. They aren't hazing us for mere pleasure, but are challenging us to produce better work.

Alternatively, we can also view reviewers as belligerent, and approach the revision process with defensiveness. We fear that these angry reviewers will invalidate our whole project. We manage that fear defensively, approaching all feedback with snarls. Not only is this posture stressful, it also makes our revision less likely to succeed. Reviewers can sense our defensiveness, and it does the opposite of win them over to recommending our article's publication.

When the revision process becomes annoying—as it certainly will—decide now to default to the noble reason. Assume that your reviewers have science's best interest in mind. Believe that the revision process will make your manuscript better.[88] Because those beliefs, though a bit naïve, are mostly true.

Take all reviewer feedback, however, with skepticism: this is your article, after all, and you decide what constitutes the Final Draft. Know when to yield and when to rebut—that is, the verb form of "rebuttal," which is genteel, peer-revision jargon for "pointing out why a reviewer's comment is full of shit." Surrender stylistic changes as long as the main message stays intact. But resist suggestions that would change the project's fundamental story. And for most comments—the ones in the grey area between those extremes—read on.

INTERNAL REVIEW

The revision process starts internally with your co-authors. During internal revision, you'll go through multiple rounds of pushing your draft to your co-authors, giving them two weeks to revise it, receiving their feedback, incorporating that feedback, and pushing out a revised draft for their further review. The reviewers might include peers, managers, other professors and your supervisor. And though you'll consider each of their feedback, your main goal is to secure your supervisor's approval to submit the manuscript to the target journal.

Feedback from your Supervisor

Your supervisor is your most important critic. For graduate students, in particular, supervisors are not only bosses but mentors. You can view feedback from your other reviewers as suggestions, but feedback from your supervisor provides an opportunity to better understand their research enterprise, and to build the manuscript more like they would. Despite your potential differences with your supervisor, it benefits you to wholly learn their methods, even if you someday deviate from them.

In the reviewal phase, this deference requires two accommodations. First, you'll incorporate most of your supervisor's edits. When your supervisor reworks the manuscript's style, it teaches you new writing tools. When they reorganize an argument, it teaches you new persuasive tactics. If they alter the main story, you may ask for clarification or, indeed, push back, but you'll learn their motivations in the process. In all cases, when your supervisor provides edits you don't understand, you have license to sit down with them that you may better hear their position, learn from it, and argue for an alternative solution if needed.

The second accommodation you'll give your supervisor is time. You'll give each of your internal reviewers a two-week deadline, but for your supervisor, that deadline has little meaning. Without their approval, you cannot complete any iteration of the revision process. So you must wait on their availability. Giving your supervisor a deadline does, however, help you encourage—i.e., bother—them by quantifying their tardiness.

When your supervisor drags their feet—whether justified or not—you have a few tools to prod them. The two-week deadline is one, but you must be careful how you use it. For your first tactic, you might try badgering. This option is rarely effective: it requires a lot of communication on your end and increased stress for both you and your supervisor.

A better tactic is to ease the underlying problem behind the tardiness. Your supervisor lacks time. They cannot do everything, so they prioritize, and your early publication drafts might simply rank low on their priority list. How can you help solve this problem? You cannot revise the draft for them, but you can help them manage the revision process: you can make time by scheduling an editing meeting, and you can efficiently use that time by preparing tasks and providing uninterrupted access to your help.[89] Politely confront your supervisor about the revision deadline, request a couple of hours on their schedule to edit the draft together, and show up prepared: bring a computer, bring a to-do list, work through the editing chapter from structure to story to paragraph, and lead the meeting agenda toward the finish line—where your supervisor approves the revision. Your supervisor's time is limited, so come prepared to help maximize that scarce time together.[90]

Feedback from Co-Authors

You'll handle your other co-authors' feedback a bit differently than your supervisor's. For one, you'll hold them more strictly to the two-week revision deadline. You should aim to get everyone's buy-in before submitting to the journal. But if after two weeks you have feedback from your supervisor and most of your co-authors, you can finish earlier rounds of revision without waiting for the straggling reviewers' comments.[91]

Another difference is that you'll give your co-authors some revision guidance. Many of your peers, for example, may lack editing experience. But they can still provide excellent comments when given some direction. Consider prompting peers with the following editorial questions:

What is the research gap and research question? Are they well supported by the Introduction?

Do the Methods omit any vital information?

Do the figures make sense?

Does the Conclusion align with the Results?

Underline any confusing sentences or paragraphs.

Circle any exciting sentences or paragraphs..

By prompting your peers with these types of questions, you'll receive helpful feedback despite their limited editing experience. Maximize that feedback by sitting down with them, one-on-one, and working out solutions to their questions.[92]

For your more experienced co-authors—postdocs, researchers, professors—you can still offer some revision guidance. If a co-author lends your project a specific technical skill, you may ask some pointed questions about their domain-specific methods and findings. If a co-author is particularly well-published, you may ask for feedback on the manuscript's structure and flow.

The last difference between your supervisor's and other co-authors' feedback: you can ignore a co-authors' suggestions. Be reasonable: incorporate good feedback, and trust specialist co-authors' domain-specific edits. But as lead author, you want to efficiently finish the revision while keeping the main story intact. For any debates that detract from that goal, you can exercise your lead-author authority and make the decision that is best for the project.

Finishing the Internal Review

Eventually you'll have most of your co-authors' feedback. But how do you reconcile their different comments—especially if they make conflicting suggestions? First, incorporate your supervisor's feedback. Then work through each co-author's review in order of their research experience. Consider implementing each comment, especially if multiple co-authors suggest the same fix, but ignore comments that detract from the manuscript's main story.

After considering each co-author's feedback, update the manuscript and repeat the revision again: send out the updated draft, give a revision deadline, incorporate feedback, update the manuscript, and send it out again.

You may finish two, three, or more rounds of internal revision. And by round two, you often notice that your co-authors do something frustrating: they make a suggestion, you implement it, then later they suggest you change things back to the original version.[93] This feels maddening. But remember that editing is tough work. There is more than one way, more than five ways to write a thing well. If your supervisor is the offender, sit down and edit with them—accomplishing the back-and-forth haggling in real time. For other offenders, use your lead author authority and make an executive decision.

The internal review is done when your supervisor is satisfied. Once they give the nod, send your co-authors the final draft, say that it is supervisor-approved, and submit it to the journal. You'll reach out again when you receive journal reviewer comments.

SUBMIT TO THE JOURNAL

Submitting your manuscript to the target journal marks a significant milestone in your publication's journey. It's also rather anti-climactic. The journal's website will have a submission procedure to follow. Double check that the manuscript meets the requirements—word count, structure, file format. Write a quick cover letter—see the appendix at the end of this book for a template. Then submit.

After you click the submit button, you'll be redirected to a congratulatory webpage with a picture of balloons and cake. Well, that's what should happen. But it doesn't. Instead, you'll get a standard email confirming your submission and explaining any next steps. You might hear from the editor early on if you need to provide any missing information. But mostly you'll just wait.

Usually, you'll wait for a few months while the editor enlists a handful of reviewers to assess your project. These anonymous reviewers must be recruited, read the manuscript, then provide detailed feedback on what you need to correct to make the article publishable. They have little incentive to do this in a timely manner. And you have little influence over the speed of this often-sluggish process. The outcome: a lot of waiting.

While you Wait

That doesn't mean, however, that you should sit around and do nothing while you wait. It may be tempting to take a research sabbatical and focus on other commitments, like finally starting that board game club. Alas, you still have productive uses for this downtime. For one, you'll need a bit of light work to maintain your hard-won work rhythm. Plus, you have a few lingering tasks to complete:

1. You can start archiving your work. That means organizing data, digitizing relevant lab notes, creating metadata for research files, and writing instructional manuals for any code or software runs. It's easier to do this now, with the project fresh on your mind, than to wait until after defending your dissertation. Moreover, the journal reviewers may request additional analysis. By organizing your data now, you can easily oblige.

2. You might also use this downtime to revisit your research rabbit trails. During the experimenting phase, you noted data outliers, tangential analyses, and other rabbit trails that spun off your main project. You were tempted to follow those leads immediately. Instead you stored those ideas in your lab notebook. Now's your chance to revisit that list of serendipitous side projects. With hindsight, you may immediately recognize a few dead ends, but some of these rabbit trails may still hold promise. Get back in the lab and prod the most promising ideas—try reproducing the curious event and gathering new data. Although you generally want questions to drive your research, a bit of unbridled wandering has its benefits.

3. You might also use this downtime to start your next project. You likely have leftover experimental data, unanswered questions, and a growing literature reading queue to get you started. Simply jump back a few chapters, begin a new literature review, and search for the next research gap.

THE JOURNAL PEER REVIEW

And then—during the middle of archiving, rabbit-trail chasing, or the next project's literature review—the journal's editor will email you back.

That email always frightens me a bit. A lot seems to hang on it. Few emails deliver so much excitement and dread at the same time. Excitement because this will likely be your last hurdle before publication. Dread because reviewers will suggest corrections—often difficult and controversial ones. Wait to open that email until the end of the day. Otherwise, your schedule will be ruined as you devote your subconscious to crafting your updated manuscript.

When you open the editor's email, you'll find two important details. First, you'll find out whether the article is rejected, accepted, or that the editor wants you to make some corrections and resubmit. If accepted, well done! An outright acceptance is incredibly rare—go buy a lottery ticket now.

If rejected, I'm sorry! Rejection is disheartening, but it's an unavoidable part of academic research.[94] Don't overthink it—it's truly not personal. Take the reviewer's feedback, make corrections to strengthen the manuscript, and submit it to your backup journal. Beware submitting it without applying at least some of the original reviewers' suggestions, though—the same reviewers may reappear for your backup journal and instantly reject an identical manuscript.[95]

Most likely, the editor will ask you to revise and resubmit. You can try to decipher the editor's posture toward your publication chances, but that's not really helpful in the end. Whether they seem to love or hate the article does not impact your response.[96] Regardless, you'll consider the reviewers' feedback and submit an updated manuscript.

The email's second important detail is the editor's and reviewers' comments. You must address each of those comments to convince the editor to accept a revised version of the manuscript. That means understanding the comments, reacting to them, and explaining your reaction to the reviewers.

A Negotiator's Mindset

Before we jump in, let's adjust our posture so that we handle the revision strategically. Remember our noble belief—that we, the editor, and the reviewers are on the same team. We're all trying to rework this manuscript into something better—something that advances science. Even the most cynical reviewers hold that sentiment somewhere in their dark hearts.

That said, we can best approach the revision process as a negotiation. We, the authors, want an unchanged manuscript. Our reviewers have many ideas for improving it. We need to find a compromise—giving enough concessions to appease the reviewers without changing the manuscript's main story. That means we will incorporate many of the reviewers' suggestions, rebut their comments when needed, and strategically pivot our responses to downplay any disagreements.

We hope to win over our reviewers. But even if we don't, our negotiation has a third party with final authority on the publication decision—the editor.[97] If the reviewers dislike our response, the editor might appreciate our respectful, accommodating compromises and publish the article anyway. Here's a general strategy for pursuing that balanced compromise:

> Realize that you can respond to a comment in three ways: incorporate the suggestion, rebut or reject the comment, or pivot by acknowledging the comment but only partially implementing it.[98]

> Attempt to agree with all suggestions. If you can pull that off, there will be little argument against publishing your revised manuscript.[99]
>
> Save your rebuttals for when the reviewer is wrong, and you believe their suggestions would weaken the manuscript or extend beyond the research project's scope.
>
> Limit rebuttals to 20% of a reviewer's comments. If you disagree with three of a reviewer's ten suggestions, rebut the worst two and pivot on the third.

Remember that you have final authority—not on publication acceptance, but on the content of your article. You can always walk away from the negotiation. But it's usually worth the effort to try some creative compromises and submit a revised manuscript, even if you doubt whether a contentious reviewer will approve the new version.

If you strike the right balance, you'll end up with a better article, content reviewers, a happy editor, and your first published journal article.

REVISE THE MANUSCRIPT

With that strategy in mind, let's revise the article. You have two main documents to prepare: 1) an updated manuscript, in which you implement changes based on the reviewers' suggestions, and 2) a "Response to Reviewers" document, where you'll respond to each of the reviewers' comments.

Start by sorting the comments by common themes and developing a to-do list of changes to make to the article. Copy all the comments into one document. Under each comment, note the applicable IMRaD section and the action you will take to address the comment. Then sort the comments by IMRaD section and action. Now you have a revision to-do list.[100]

But before you revise the article, consider which to-do items you'll actually incorporate. Again, if you can incorporate all of them, there will be little argument against publishing your article. But that is often impractical: you must usually respond to a few comments with pivoting or rebuttal. The rest of the chapter advises how to decide your course of action.

Then, create your "Response to Reviewers" document.[101] For each of the reviewers' comments, acknowledge the suggestion, answer the reviewer's question, describe the changes you made to the article, and reproduce the article's updated text. That may sound like overkill, but it makes the reviewers' jobs easier—and happy reviewers are a good thing to cultivate. For a content and formatting example, see the appendix for a "Response to Reviewers" template.

Finally, remember that you aren't alone during the peer-review process. Your supervisor, at least, will want to be involved and your co-authors should be happy to pitch in—a nearly-published article sits high on most people's priority list. After planning your revision and response, solicit help tackling any reviewer comments that confuse or overwhelm you.

That workflow—sort the comments, revise the manuscript, respond to reviewers—gives some general guidance, but let's discuss some specific directions. What's the most efficient way to update the manuscript? What response do you give the reviewers? How do you gracefully rebut and pivot? It all depends on the type of comment.

You'll see a few different types of comments from your reviewers. In order of increasing difficulty, we have:

> Grammar comments: the reviewer suggests some ideas for improving the article's writing.
>
> Clarifying questions: the reviewer finds some part of the project confusing.
>
> Objections: the reviewer challenges the project's accuracy, novelty, or validity.
>
> Incomprehensible statements: the reviewer produces a poorly-worded, unclear comment.

In the following pages, we'll discuss each of these comment types, their underlying motivations, and how you can best respond to them.

HANDLING GRAMMAR COMMENTS

A reviewer might correct the manuscript's grammar, wording, abbreviations, formatting, or other writing-related items. These suggestions are often generic, but reviewers occasionally correct specific sentences in the article. These comments may feel a bit particular, but they provide easy opportunities to marginally improve the manuscript.

You should almost always incorporate reviewers' nit-picky writing suggestions. Even if a suggestion isn't quite grammatically correct, if it doesn't weaken the writing, it's more strategic to implement the reviewer's advice rather than debate negligible grammar errors.

A reviewer might also comment on the manuscript's story and structure. They might suggest that you broaden your Introduction's motivation to reach a larger audience, more explicitly state your research question, reorder your Results & Discussion to better highlight the main findings, or otherwise improve the article's story. This rare type of structural feedback can be extremely insightful. If it strengthens the article, then implement it. But if the comment seems a bit off, or if it clashes with your writing style, you can pivot by redirecting the comment toward a slightly different, more generic issue.

In the Response to Reviewers document:

To implement the reviewer's suggestion

1. Briefly thank the reviewer for pointing out the error.

2. Describe your correction.

3. Reproduce the corrected sentence.

To pivot on a structural suggestion

1. Acknowledge the underlying concern—for example, that your main finding lacks emphasis.

2. Describe what changes you made to the manuscript to address that concern.

3. Reproduce the updated sentences and paragraphs—or at least the most important ones—below your response.

HANDLING CLARIFYING QUESTIONS

A reviewer might be confused about a particular part of the article. They might simply declare their confusion without any actual suggestions, or they might present their confusion as a question that asks for clarification. In either case, the comment is less important than the underlying issue—something about your project is unclear, and you need to fix it.

You cannot respond to these questions by simply answering them in your Response to Reviewers document; you must revise the manuscript to invalidate the question altogether. That means you must identify the underlying issue that caused the lack of clarity, correct it, and connect it to the reviewer's question. That involves pivoting.

In the Response to Reviewers document:

1. Acknowledge the reviewer's confusion and thank them for bringing it to your attention.

2. Answer the reviewer's specific question directly.

3. Describe how their question helped you identify an underlying problem with the manuscript.

4. Describe how you fixed that problem, how that fix improves the article's clarity, and how that increased clarity will prevent your readers from experiencing the same confusion.

5. Reproduce the updated manuscript text.

HANDLING OBJECTIONS

A reviewer might identify a flaw in your project. These comments span from dispassionate, objective statements to belligerent, condescending remarks. Regardless, they communicate the same message—you must fix this issue for the manuscript to be published.

Your response depends on the objection's target. So let's describe some possible variations on these objections and discuss your options for resolving them. And when in doubt, you can always check in with your supervisor and co-authors for help.

Misunderstandings

A reviewer might object to a problem that doesn't actually exist; their objection is based on a misunderstanding. This type of comment is similar to a clarifying question, except it carries a more objectionable tone.

Since these comments rarely suggest improvements, you cannot directly implement them, and your best course of action is to pivot. Like the clarifying question, you must identify the underlying issue that caused the reviewer's misunderstanding and then correct it.

In the Response to Reviewers document, you'll handle these comments similarly to clarifying questions, but with more focus on diffusing the reviewer's objections. That means a more detailed response to the reviewer's particular objection. Specifically:

1. Apologize for the confusion. Validate the reviewer by agreeing that their objection would be an important

one to address. But tell them that their objection is based on a misunderstanding.

2. Point out the error in the manuscript that created the misunderstanding.

3. Describe how you corrected that error. Discuss how that correction removes the misunderstanding from the article.

4. Reproduce the updated manuscript text.

Research Gap

A reviewer might object to your research gap. They might object generally: "the project lacks novelty." Or they might explicitly point out aspects of the research gap that the literature already fills. This is a serious comment. You must handle it carefully. If you poorly explain the research gap, then your research question—not to mention the entire project—lacks a solid foundation.

These comments are challenging to rebut: you must prove that you understand the literature better than your reviewer does, and invalidate their argument. That's a major uphill battle. So even if the comment has some flaws, your best course of action is to pivot.

You can pivot by acknowledging that the research gap is too broad, finding some new literature that elaborates the research gap, and defining a new, narrower research gap that dodges the reviewer's objections and can still be answered by your experimental findings.

This requires some rewriting of the article:

1. Create a narrower research gap. This can be a subtle change, depending on the reviewer's severity, but you must change something. And you must support that change with some additional literature review.

2. Update the Introduction's background section to include any new citations. Update any literature summaries to incorporate the new information.

3. Incorporate one or more of these new citations into the Discussion section.

4. Update the Conclusion with the new research gap.

5. Additionally, consider adjusting the research question to match the new gap. If you adjust the research question, be sure that your findings still answer it, and then update it throughout the manuscript.

That level of thoroughness shows the reviewer that you took their comment seriously. It also provides a strong argument for your project's novelty, which should appease the reviewer's objection.

In the Response to Reviewers document:

1. Thank the reviewer for pointing out their concerns about the project's novelty.

2. Describe how you expanded your literature review to more accurately frame the research gap. List the new citations, and make an effort to find citations less than three years old. If the reviewer suggests specific citations, use them or explain why they've been excluded.

3. State the new, narrower research gap.

4. Describe the changes you made to the manuscript to accommodate that new research gap.

5. Reproduce the updated manuscript text.

Literature Review and Background

A reviewer might object to the incompleteness of your literature review. Either you've omitted a few important publications, or you've overlooked a whole niche research area. These objections rarely invalidate your project, but they accuse you of underrepresenting other researchers' work.

These comments are difficult to rebut: you would need to argue that additional background information would detract from your manuscript—a tough sell. The best response is to accept the reviewer's suggestion and expand your literature discussion. If the reviewer suggests some specific articles to reference, you should include them or explain why you excluded them. And then, similar to responding to a research gap objection, find a handful of recently published articles, add them to the Introduction's background, reword any literature summaries to include them, and incorporate these new citations in the Methods and Discussion as appropriate.

In the Response to Reviewers document:

1. Thank the reviewer for pointing out deficiencies in the literature review.

2. Agree to expand the background information.

3. Describe how you expanded your literature review to

more accurately frame the research gap. List the new citations, including some articles less than three years old. If the reviewer suggests specific citations, use them or explain why they've been excluded.

4. Describe the changes you made to the manuscript to incorporate these new citations.

5. Reproduce the updated manuscript text.

Methods

A reviewer might object to the theory, data, apparatus, procedure, analysis, or other aspects of your experiment. In other words, the reviewer has identified an experimental limitation.

Limitations vary in their severity, both in how strongly the limitation undermines your project—from trivial to significant—and in the amount of work required to fix the limitation—from minor update to major overhaul. Your course of action depends on where the reviewer's comment sits along those two continuums.

For objections that require minor experimental updates—reprocessing some output data, improving your statistical analysis, etc.—simply implement those suggestions. You must, consequently, update the Methods, figures, tables, and Results, and you might need to update the Conclusion.

In the Response to Reviewers document:

1. Thank the reviewer for their suggestion.

2. Describe your updates to the project.

3. Describe your changes to the manuscript.

4. Reproduce the updated manuscript text.

For objections that reveal trivial limitations but require a major experimental overhaul, you should pivot: you'll keep the current Methods but update the Limitations. If the limitation is, indeed, trivial then you can explain it away by citing publications with similar limitations. You'll acknowledge the reviewer's argument but use the literature to invalidate it.

This can be done by adding a short paragraph to your Methods Limitations section and by updating the various limitations' summaries throughout manuscript. Here's an example Limitations paragraph:

> "We assume [such and such assumption] when performing our experiment. This might seem like a limitation, but the fact that [explaining away the significance of the weakness] means that the assumption has a negligible impact on the experiment's outcomes. Consequently, other researchers have made similar assumptions when using the same experimental method. [Citations here]"

The context provided by this additional paragraph should appease the reviewer and inform your readers without undermining your work.

In the Response to Reviewers document:

1. Thank the reviewer for their comment.

2. Agree that your readers might have similar misgivings about the method.

3. Explain how studies with similar assumptions show that the limitation has little influence on the results.

4. Describe the changes you made to the manuscript to incorporate these new citations.

5. Reproduce the updated Limitations paragraph.

For objections that reveal significant limitations and require a major experimental overhaul, you're in a tough situation. You can try to pivot, but if the limitations significantly undermine your work, you might have to adjust the research gap, research question, Results, and Conclusion to accommodate the stricter limitation and the narrower scope that it requires. That much rewriting will weaken your manuscript and might fail to satisfy the reviewer. The better option—and the more difficult one—is to overhaul the methods and redo the experiment. This is a bitter outcome: it may require substantial effort. We tried to avoid it by reviewing the literature and outlining our Methods before we began our experiment, but sometimes we make mistakes.

Finally, a reviewer might suggest a Methods update that is truly tangential to the project's scope. The reviewer may suggest that these improved methods are an opportunity to strengthen the project. But you know better, because you see that the resulting output would not help to answer your research question. You could pivot, but for your readers' sake, you don't really want to discuss the reviewer's obscure idea in the manuscript. So for these types of comments, you'll rebut.

In the Response to Reviewers document:

1. Thank the reviewer for their suggestion.

2. Agree that it would be an interesting experiment.

3. Suggest that the method does not align with the research question as appropriately as your current methods do.

4. Point the reviewer toward the publications that support your methods choice.

Results

A reviewer may object to your results. Typically, they either object to the quantity—recommending more data, tables, and figures—or they object to the quality.

For objections to quality, the reviewer will likely point out errors or misrepresentations in the way you present the data. In either case you can typically accept these suggestions: your article benefits from clearer, more accurate findings. Simply rework your results, tables, and figures, update the Results & Discussion accordingly, and adjust the Conclusion if needed.

In your Response to the Reviewers document:

1. Thank the reviewer for their suggestion.

2. Agree that the new findings will improve the study.

3. Describe how you implemented the suggestions.

4. Reproduce the updated manuscript text.

For objections to quantity, the reviewer will probably suggest additional data, figures, and experimental output they would like to see. You must be careful in obliging these requests. Remember that curiosity can drive you to include too many findings, tables, and figures in the First Draft, which distracts from the main story. Reviewers fall prey to the same curiosity. If their suggestion strays from the main story and would distract the reader, then rebut it.

Besides keeping the manuscript on point, these rebuttals also have practical advantages: the fewer data, tables, and figures you publish in this manuscript, the more you'll save for your next project. I've heard sad stories of researchers who give up two or three publications-worth of findings to appease their journal reviewers. They end up with a bloated publication, and extra years of labor to complete their next project. Data are difficult to produce but easy to give away. And when the quantity of your publications is important, you should save extra data for your next project rather than use them to appease a reviewer.

In the Response to Reviewers document:

1. Thank the reviewer for their suggestions.

2. Agree that the additional results would be interesting.

3. But point out that they stray off-topic from the research question. Be sure to note—for the editor's eyes—that you fear these new results would be tangential to the research question, lengthen the article, and distract readers from the main findings.

Interpretations and Conclusions

A reviewer may object to your interpretation of the findings and to the conclusions that you infer from those interpretations. Your response depends on the objection's severity.

The objection might center around semantics. The reviewer might suggest toning down a claim, or highlighting an important caveat. In this case, you'll usually implement their feedback. It's easy to conclude an article with grand gestures about how your project advances science. This pageantry is okay unless it overblows your findings. Reviewers do a good job keeping these claims realistic.

To respond, simply implement their suggestion, and update any other parts of the manuscript affected by that adjustment—i.e., the introduction to the Results, and parts of the Discussion, Conclusion, abstract, and possibly the end of the Introduction.

In the Response to Reviewers document:

1. Thank the reviewer for their comment.

2. Agree that the update will improve the study.

3. Describe how you implemented the suggestions.

4. Reproduce the updated manuscript text.

Alternatively, the reviewer's objection might invalidate some of your conclusions. If so, you can pivot. Pivot by adjusting your interpretations and conclusions to maintain your overall story while acknowledging the reviewer's position. It may help to expand the Discussion section—perhaps with some new citations—to put your conclusions more firmly in the context of the literature. This can help your conclusions seem more reasonable.

In the Response to Reviewers document:

1. Thank the reviewer for sharing their concerns.

2. Agree that they make some valid points and that you don't want to incorrectly interpret your findings.

3. Describe how you've updated your interpretations and conclusions to include the reviewer's feedback.

4. Then add how you expanded the Discussion section to provide more context for the updated interpretations. You might explicitly point out that your conclusions align with the expectations, trends, or interpretations typical of similar publications.

5. Reproduce the updated manuscript text.

HANDLING INCOMPREHENSIBLE STATEMENTS

A reviewer might make some rambling, incomprehensible statement. You won't understand what the reviewer is asking, let alone how to answer it.

These situations are awkward. It isn't helpful to write back for clarification. This correspondence can take weeks, and—to your disadvantage—it makes the reviewer feel foolish. Your best option is to concoct some manuscript improvement that you can connect to the comment's general theme. First, check the other reviewers' comments for a similar statement. If you find something suitable, you can answer the incomprehensible statement using your response to the other reviewer's similar comment. Otherwise, reword the incomprehensible statement into a more concrete question that you can reasonably answer.

Then, answer that reworded version of the question and respond to the reviewer as if that's the question they intended to ask all along.

This tactic feels a bit sheepish because your response will read awkwardly next to the reviewer's original comment. But it puts you in a surprisingly strategic position because the reviewer lacks a legitimate response. When the reviewer reads your reply, they'll only have a few options for responding.

They might see that you gave a positive reply, and simply move on. Reviewers sometimes fixate on the rebuttals rather than the agreements.

They might forget the original intent of their incomprehensible comment. In that case, they can't reasonably refute your response. The best they can do is assume you correctly understood their intent and that you gave a reasonable answer—especially if you accepted most of their other comments with reasonable responses.

Or they will, in fact, remember the comment's original intent and notice that you misunderstood. In that case, they could send a new comment clarifying what they actually meant. But that makes the reviewer appear foolish, and it wastes the editor's time. Usually, the reviewer will let it go and be content with your responses to the rest of their comments.

That gives you an idea of the type of comments you'll see during peer review and some strategies for how to respond. Get feedback from your supervisor and co-authors on any confusing comments, significant changes to the project, or noteworthy updates to the manuscript. When you've answered all of the reviewers' comments by updating the manuscript and completing your Response to Reviewers document, you can submit the revision to the journal. Then get ready for more waiting.

PUBLISHED

Eventually, you'll get an email back from the editor. Either the reviewers have a few lingering concerns for you to address, or the revision was approved and the article will be published.

I know you're imagining it now—you get that email, the article is published, and you waltz into a springtime montage with flowers, peppy music, and high-fives from all of your department's National Academy members. The lackluster reality: waivers, proofs, and back-and-forth about formatting changes and document uploads. The real end—when the typeset article shows up online and people can actually download it—is still a couple of weeks away.

And given all of your labors, this conclusion will, sadly, feel anticlimactic. You're probably working on your next project by now, and this lingering publication process has become more nuisance than triumph.

But don't let the anticlimax stifle the victory. You've come a long way through the research process. You started with a hunch about a research topic. You used the literature to expand that hunch into a research gap. You developed that gap into a research question and a detailed research plan. You produced experimental data to answer that research question. You transformed that data into high-quality visualizations of your findings. You compiled your work into an engaging scientific story. You edited that story into a crisp, readable manuscript. And you maneuvered that manuscript through a lengthy revision process that matured it into a published journal article. The end result is not perfect. But it's above average, it advances science, and it improves society. And that's a triumph worth celebrating.

Chapter Recap

The revision process matures our Second Draft into a publishable journal article. Revision is a slow process that involves both an internal review with our co-authors and a formal peer review with the journal. It is most successful and least frustrating when we release our defensiveness and trust our reviewer's good intentions.

In the internal review, we solicited feedback from our co-authors, incorporated their comments, sent an updated draft for additional feedback, and repeated. Although we received helpful comments from all of our co-authors, we prioritized the feedback from our supervisor. We accepted most of our supervisor's suggestions, discussed any disagreements, and repeated the internal revision process until our supervisor approved the manuscript for submission to the journal.

In the journal review, an editor solicited feedback from anonymous reviewers to comment on how our article must improve before it is publishable. This process involved a lot of waiting. While we waited, we maintained our work rhythm by archiving our project, revisiting experimental rabbit trails, or starting our next project.

The journal editor eventually emailed us back, likely with a request to revise and resubmit our article along with a list of the reviewers' suggestions for how to improve it. We didn't incorporate all of the reviewers' suggestions—we also rebutted and pivoted. But by approaching the revision as a negotiation, we realized the benefits of choosing our battles wisely and aiming for a good compromise that appeased the reviewers, won over the editor, and strengthened the project.

Our revision included an updated manuscript along with a detailed Response to Reviewers document, which responded to all of our reviewers' comments. Our actions and responses depended on the nature of the comments: we handled grammar comments, clarifying questions, objections, and incomprehensible statements differently. For each of these comments, and particularly for the objections, we discussed whether to implement, rebut, or pivot, and described detailed strategies for updating the manuscript and Response to Reviewers document accordingly.

See the following page for the revision phase flowchart. See the appendix for a Journal Submission Cover Letter template and a Response to Reviewers template. Download full-sized templates and additional resources from:

www.ProductiveAcademic.com/published

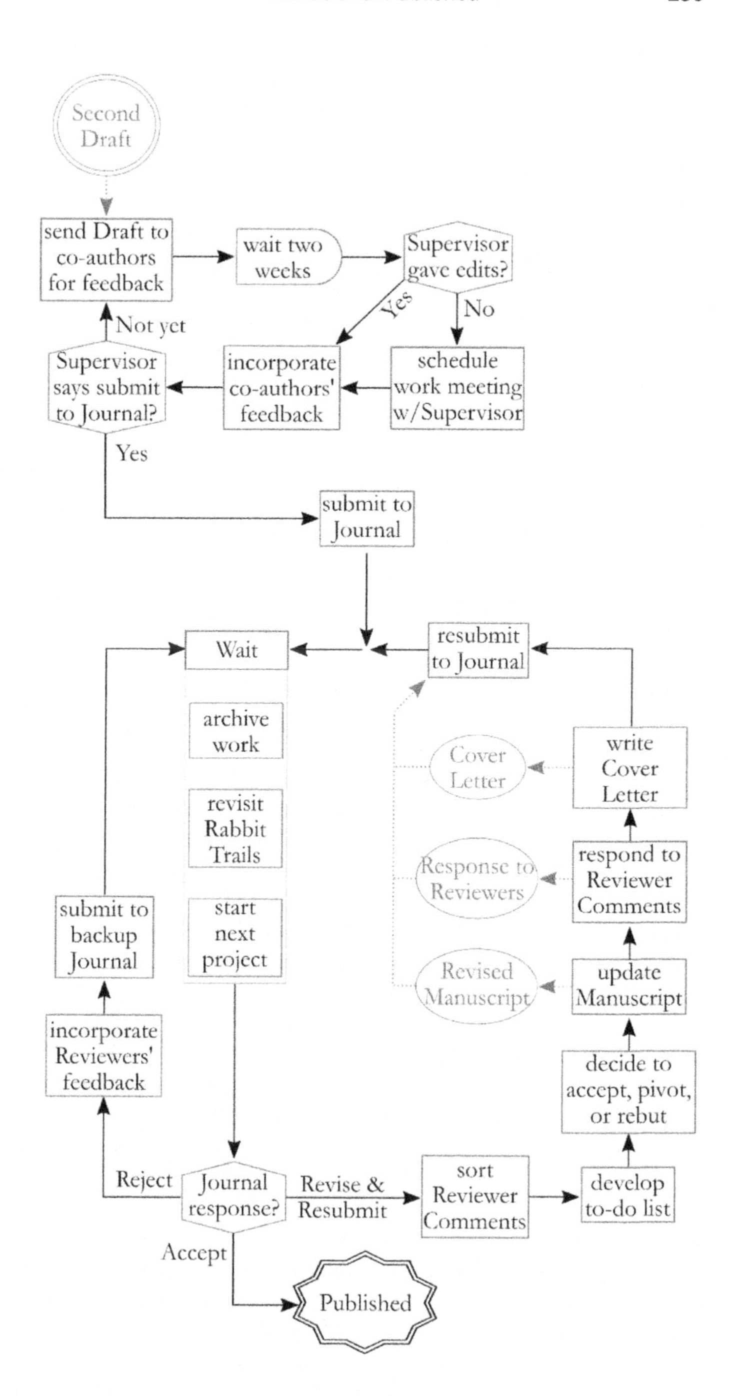
Second Draft
send Draft to co-authors for feedback
wait two weeks
Supervisor gave edits?
Yes
No
Not yet
Supervisor says submit to Journal?
incorporate co-authors' feedback
schedule work meeting w/Supervisor
Yes
submit to Journal
Wait
resubmit to Journal
archive work
revisit Rabbit Trails
start next project
Cover Letter
write Cover Letter
Response to Reviewers
respond to Reviewer Comments
Revised Manuscript
update Manuscript
submit to backup Journal
incorporate Reviewers' feedback
decide to accept, pivot, or rebut
Reject
Journal response?
Revise & Resubmit
sort Reviewer Comments
develop to-do list
Accept
Published

Epilogue: What Next?

With your first publication behind you, let's acknowledge that the process wasn't easy. Sometimes it was exciting. Often it was tedious. But always it was work. You finished it, though, and that puts you in a small group of people—people who will endure that sort of torment to contribute a small offering toward advancing scientific knowledge and improving society.

And with a published article behind you, you are now free to consider the aftermath. Maybe you just feel exhausted. That project took it all out of you, and you never want to publish another damn thing again. It's good to admit that, and there's no shame in having looked the publication process in the eye and decided that it's not a battle you want to fight again.

But if you came away from the process feeling energized, like you did something worthwhile, like you excelled at some parts of it, and you could do it even better next time, then it's time to work out your broader vision for what to do next.

Write more Articles

With your first publication behind you, let's also acknowledge that the final manuscript is nothing extraordinary. It's a useful, above-average publication, but in the large sea of research literature, your journal article's impact will be modest.

That's okay. You don't need your first publication to make substantial scientific gains. You need it to teach you how to complete a journal article so you can confidently publish again. You're just getting started.

Years from now you'll have a towering stack of journal publications. That's good, because most individual articles make only a marginal impact. But multiple publications can generate momentum in exciting new research directions.[102] That's encouraging: it means that you have many more opportunities to publish your work and increase your impact.

But that may also feel daunting. Producing a stack of published journal articles requires great effort and time; you can only produce so much. But if you acknowledge that limitation now, you can plan for it strategically. So finish more experiments and publish more articles. But only pursue your best ideas. And focus those ideas on one topic area that can support a series of publications in the direction of a potential breakthrough.

Start with the leftover Impressions from your literature review. Look for potential research gaps and unanswered questions. Revisit the experimental rabbit trails from your lab notes. Consider the overzealous suggestions from journal reviewers. And keep your research momentum by brainstorming your next two projects. It will be a lot of work, but now you have the confidence to attack it.

Perfect your Research Process

Before starting those projects in earnest, though, take some time to reevaluate everything you've done so far. This book prescribes an effective research process. It combines my experience with a lot of guidance written by other academic researchers. But things that work for me, even things that work for most people, might not work well for you. That's okay, because following someone else's guidance gives you enough experience to begin customizing your own research process. This book is just a starting point.

With your first research project behind you, consider how you would improve the research process to better fit your style:

> Which research phases did you find difficult?
>
> How will you manage those difficulties during your next project?
>
> Which research phases came naturally?
>
> Which of your skills, interests, or strengths aided you during those easier phases?
>
> How will you use those strengths in your next project?

And if you have time, reread this book. Note the instructions that you would improve. Note the ones that you thought were dead on. And note the ones that, even though they were a lot of work, you enjoyed them and felt like you thrived on them. And let those adjustments evolve into a custom research process that fits your unique style.

Show Others How

For the parts of the research process that you most enjoyed and for the tasks that you excelled at, share those strengths with others. Find ways to develop those competencies and use them to advance other researchers' projects. Often that contribution will be reciprocated: you'll find that other academics with an interdependent mindset are more than happy to work with someone who has developed their individual strengths and is eager to share them with others. And also remember the many people who have helped you along the way. You cannot pay them all back, but without their help you would still be stuck somewhere further back than where you are now. If you really care about advancing science and improving society, then help others achieve the same goal—it's a valuable use of your time.

That basically sums up what I've tried to do with this book. I enjoy breaking complex tasks into systems, explaining them in simple language, and communicating through writing. I wanted to apply those skills to help novice researchers break through some of the barriers that made it difficult for me to complete my first, and second, and tenth publications. Writing a book seemed like the best way to achieve that.

If you found the book helpful, recommend it to a friend, and leave an honest review online. If this really *is* a helpful book, more reviews will help it reach more researchers like you—researchers who need help getting published.

And thankfully for all of us, there are other people who have written books that share their particular talents. If you want to expand the skills you feel naturally gifted in, this book only covers the high points. But its notes and selected references point to other books that dive deeper into the different research phases. Consider reading them to improve your skill—we'll all benefit from it.

Appendix of Templates

The following pages contain templates referred to throughout the book. In particular, these templates will help you visualize some of the writing structures I attempted to describe in the book's main text.

Given the physical dimensions of this book, the templates have been compressed, abridged, and given smaller fonts than I would have fit in an 8.5"x11" version. But I wanted to include the compressed versions in the book so that you could find all the relevant material you would need between its front and back covers without having to download the templates elsewhere. If helpful, however, you can download full-sized, 8.5"x11" versions of these templates from:

www.ProductiveAcademic.com/published

Ch.5: Literature Note-taking Template

Author Last Name, Journal article title
Journal name (Publication year)

Research Question

Look near the end of the Introduction: Write a one-sentence summary of the article's research question. If the article gives a hypothesis, write a one-sentence summary of that too.

Motivation

Look near the beginning of the article's Introduction: Write a one-sentence summary of the social motivation. How will the article solve social, environmental, or other problems?

Look throughout the Introduction's Background/Lit Review portion: Write a one sentence summary of the research gap. How will the article fill a lack of knowledge in the literature?

Results

Look in the Results & Discussion, especially the figures, tables, and subsection headers: Write a one-sentence summary of the main finding. What finding directly answers the research question?

Write a one-sentence summary of each supplementary finding. What context do these supplementary findings add to the main finding?

Copy and paste any relevant figures and/or tables.

Methods

Look in the Methods section: Write a one-paragraph summary of the experimental methods. Describe each phase of the experiment, how those phases interact, what inputs they require, and what outputs they generate. Draw a flowchart for complex methods.

Impressions

Answer the following questions:

How can you adjust the article's research question to better fit its motivation?

Does the article's answer to the research question fully fill its identified research gap?

What are the study's limitations? How could you reduce those limitations?

What assumptions does the study make? Are those assumptions correct? If not, how must the study change if those assumptions are abandoned?

Ch.5: Literature Synopsis Template

Ledger

For each article in your literature review, paste from your individual notes:

[Article_1 AuthorLastName] [Article_1 title] [Article_1 Publication Year]
Your one-sentence version of Article_1's research question
Your one-sentence summary of Article_1's methods

[Article_2 AuthorLastName] [Article_2 title] [Article_2 Publication Year]
Your one-sentence version of Article_2's research question
Your one-sentence summary of Article_2's methods

...

[Article_N AuthorLastName] [Article_N title] [Article_N Publication Year]
Your one-sentence version of Article_N's research question
Your one-sentence summary of Article_N's methods

Impressions

For each article in your literature review, paste the Impressions from your individual notes. Cite each Impression. As this synopsis grows, reorganize the notes by common themes—this will help you notice questions, criticisms, or weaknesses that span multiple articles.

[Theme 1]

A question, criticism, or weakness about Article_1. ([cite Article_1])
A related question, criticism, or weakness about Article_2. ([cite Article_2])
A related question, criticism, or weakness about Article_N. ([cite Article_N])

[Theme 2]

A question, criticism, or weakness about Article_2. ([cite Article_2])
A related question, criticism, or weakness about Article_N. ([cite Article_N])

...

[Theme X]

A question, criticism, or weakness about Article_N. ([cite Article_N)
A related question, criticism, or weakness about Article_Z. ([cite Article_Z])

Ch.6: Project Outline Template 1/2

Introduction

How does my research project improve society?
[Your answer to the question here.]

What are some publications with similar motivations?
[Summary sentence of a broad research motivation that covers many articles.]
[One-sentence summary of an article's research motivation. Cite article.]
[One-sentence summary of an article's research motivation. Cite article.]

Research Gap
[Weakness A]:
[Your summary of the weakness]
[Your description of the niche research area where that weakness is evident.]
[Impressions from your Literature Synopsis relevant to Weakness A. Cite relevant articles.]

[Other Weaknesses in the literature]:
follow format of Weakness A above

Research Gap:
[Describe the research gap. Combine the weaknesses to show a broader gap in the literature.]

Research Question
[Your main research question.] *(This is the outline's most important sentence.)*
[Supplementary questions that provide context to the main research question.]

What publications have similar research questions?
[Summary sentence of a broad research question that covers many articles.]
[One-sentence summary of an article's research question. One-sentence summary of articles' experimental methods. Cite article.]
[One-sentence summary of an article's research question. One-sentence summary of articles' experimental methods. Cite article.]

How does my research question fill the research gap?
[Your answer to the question here.]

Ch.6: Project Outline Template 2/2

Methods

What are the stages of my experiment?

Data (or other experiment stage)

What actions must I accomplish in the Data phase?

[Your answer here. Be detailed. Feel free to add flow charts, outlines, or other organization tools.]

What data do I expect those actions to produce?

[Your answer here. Be detailed. Feel free to add flow charts, outlines, or other organization tools.]

What publications provide precedents to defend those actions?

[Summary sentence of a broad Data procedure that covers many articles.]
[Summary of an article's Data technique. Cite article.]
[Summary of an article's Data technique. Cite article.]

[Additional Experimental Stages]

(follow the format of the Data subsection above.)

Results & Discussion

What experimental results will answer the research question?

[Main Result]:

[Your main result here. Brainstorm one or two figures or tables, and write a couple of paragraphs about the result, variables, and relationships you would like to see.]

What publications show similar finding?

[Summary sentence of a broad result or conclusion that covers many articles.]
[One-sentence summary of an article's relevant finding. Cite article.]
[Relevant figure from the cited publication.]
[One-sentence summary of an article's relevant finding. Cite article.]
[Relevant figure from the cited publication.]

[Additional Supplementary Results]:

(follow the format of the Main Result above.)

Ch.9: Paragraph Outline Template 1/5

1. Introduction

1.1 Motivation Paragraphs

¶-1 *Broad Motivation:* To start this first paragraph, describe a broad scientific or social problem that your research will address. Then describe a smaller component of that problem. Then a smaller component still. Continue narrowing down until you reach a unique problem that your research will address. After reading this paragraph, the reader should know your niche problem and how it contributes to a wider, more significant problem.

¶-2 *Specific Research Topic:* The previous paragraph focuses on problems; this paragraph focuses on the science attempting to solve those problems. Start this paragraph with something like, "To solve [niche problem], researchers are [description of your broader research field." Then, as in the previous paragraph, use narrower and narrower descriptions to travel from your broad research discipline down to your specific research topic.

1.2 Background/Literature Review Section

¶-1 *Literature Precedent:* Introduce how the literature currently addresses the specific research topic. This paragraph acts as an introduction to summarize the rest of the Background. It introduces each of the research area subtopics that you'll discuss in the following paragraphs.

¶-2.1* *Weakness Scope:* A short paragraph—introduce the research area that relates to a particular literature weakness. Describe the various aspects of the area—methods, focus, results—and cite a handful of relevant publications.

¶-2.2* *Weakness References:* Describe a few key publications in that research area. Elaborate a small number of articles whose research techniques you will cite in the Methods, or whose research results you will cite in the Discussion. Highlight the articles' contributions and point out any shortcomings. These shortcomings should provide examples of how individual studies in this subtopic display the weakness you are identifying.

¶-2.3* *Weakness Synthesis:* A short paragraph—synthesize the previous paragraph's shortcomings into a broader weakness in the literature. Identify the omissions, caveats, limitations, invalid assumptions, or other gaps that define this particular weakness.

**(Repeat the paragraphs 2.1-2.3 for each weakness you wish to discuss. Usually two or three weaknesses provide enough information to build a research gap.)*

Ch.9: Paragraph Outline Template 2/5

1.3 Research Question Paragraphs

¶-1 *Research Gap:* After identifying a few different weaknesses in the literature, synthesize those weaknesses into one cohesive void in the literature—the research gap. That gap tells the reader what the literature does not know.

¶-2 *Research Question:* Given the research gap, describe the research question that your project will answer. This may include some supplementary questions, but identify one overarching question that those supplementary questions fit underneath. Include a hypothesis if needed.

1.4 Closing Paragraphs

¶-1 *Additional References:* You may need to cite some additional publications that don't contribute to the research gap, and weren't cited in the Background section. You might, for example, use experimental methods from a different research field. Cite those types of publications here as succinctly as possible. You can elaborate these references later—e.g. in the Methods or Discussion section—but it is helpful to introduce them now. The most efficient way to do that is to start this paragraph like, "To answer this research question, we apply [such and such methods] from [such and such research field]. [Researcher Name 1], for example, use [method 1] to study [research question 1], and [Researcher Name 2] use [method 2] to study [research question 2]."

¶-2 *Closing:* This last paragraph describes how answering your research question will advance science and improve society. It ties the research question back to the Introduction's broader motivations; it reiterates the Introduction's main points in reverse. For example, "By addressing [research question], this project fills [research gap]. Filling that research gap advances [niche research topic area] by [description of how the project advances the topic]. These advancements improve our understanding of [connection to broader scientific field]. That improved understanding helps to [connection to narrow motivation], which contributes to solving [broad motivation]."

2. Methods

2.1 Summary Paragraphs

¶-1 *Opening:* Repeat the research question, describe the experimental data that will answer the research question, then summarize the experiment that will produce that data.

¶-2 *Overview:* Give a one-sentence summary of each Methods stage/subsection. For each subsection's one-sentence summary in this paragraph, state what was done and why.

Ch.9: Paragraph Outline Template 3/5

¶-3 *Limitations:* Provide a one-sentence summary of each limitation. End this paragraph with a sentence describing how, despite the limitations, your experiment adequately answers the research question. For example, "Despite these limitations, our experiment produces statistically significant data that show [very broad results summary, e.g. 'how variable X relates to variable Y under Z circumstances'] to answer [research question]."

2.2* Experiment Stages Sections

¶-1 *Summarize:* Describe the experiment stage and why you use this particular technique.

¶-2 *Elaborate:* These paragraphs describe the technique with enough detail for the reader's general understanding. These paragraphs should progress logically. In these paragraphs, you might also elaborate publications whose methods you've built on.

¶-3 *Transition:* Connect to the next subsection. For example, describe how this stage's output becomes input data for the next experiment phase.

(Repeat section 2.2 for each stage of the experiment, e.g. Data, Samples, Apparatus, etc.)

2.3 Limitations Section

¶-1* *Experiment Limitation:* Start this paragraph with a quick introductory sentence: for example, "Our experiment is limited by [Limitation A] and [Limitation B]." Then elaborate each limitation in this and the next paragraphs.

(Repeat paragraph 1 for each of the experiment's limitations.)

¶-2 *Minimize the Limitations:* Describe how, despite the experiment's limitations, its output data adequately answer the research question. For example, "Despite these limitations, the experiment produces data suitable for answering the research question. The data show how [variable X relates to variable Y under Z circumstances]. Our analysis shows these findings to be statistically significant."

2.4 Closing Paragraphs

¶-1 *Closing:* Reiterate the whole experiment—i.e. summarize each subsection—and remind the reader how the output data produces findings that answer the research question. This paragraph should mimic the Methods first two paragraphs.

Ch.9: Paragraph Outline Template 4/5

3. Results & Discussion

3.1 Opening Paragraphs

¶-1 *Opening:* Reiterate the research question and foreshadow how your results will answer it. Focus on the main finding, but don't go too deep into the details yet. For example, "To answer [research question] we show how [variable X relates to variable Y under Z circumstances]. Our results show that [more specific language about the relationship between variable X and Y], which we elaborate in the following section."

3.2* Findings Sections

¶-1 *Summarize:* This paragraph summarizes all of the information in the rest of the subsection. Begin by describing the finding in more detail than the subtitle does.

¶-2 *Segue to Figure:* Briefly introduce the figure. Explain what data the figure shows and how those data support the finding.

¶-3 *Elaborate the Figure:* Discuss the figure in more detail. Describe important features of the figure's data—trends, outliers, intersections, etc.—that add context to the finding.

¶-4 *Interpret the Finding:* Translate the finding into new knowledge. Take the finding's objective facts and interpret them into conclusions that are relevant to answering the research question. Move this paragraph to the Discussion Section if needed.

¶-5 *Apply the Interpretation:* Take your conclusion from the previous paragraph. Use it to describe how the finding addresses the research question, or use it to describe how the finding elaborates the main finding.

¶-6 *Broaden the Interpretation:* Take the conclusion and its application from the last two paragraphs and apply it to the broader literature. Discuss how it fills the research gap or how it can be generalized to comment on your broader research field. Compare your findings to other publications'.

**(Repeat section 3.2 for each of the supplementary findings.)*

Ch.9: Paragraph Outline Template 5/5

3.3 Conclusion Section

¶-1 *Reiterate the Project*: Reiterate the research question, methods summary, and main finding. For example, "To answer [research question], we [summary of the experiment.] The experimental data show how [variable X relates to variable Y under Z circumstances]."

¶-2 *Reiterate the Limitations:* Briefly repeat the limitations. End the paragraph with something like, "Despite these limitations, our experiment adequately answers the research question because [provide some supporting argument here that mimics the Minimize the Limitations paragraph in the Methods]."

¶-3 *Answer the Research Question:* Reiterate the main result and main conclusion and describe how they answer the research question. Summarize how any supplementary findings elaborate the main finding and conclusion. Repeat any important Discussion points.

¶-4 *Generalize*: Mimic the Introduction's second paragraph. Use your results to make general conclusions about your larger research field. You might discuss how your results changed the research gap and how those changes might influence your broader research field.

¶-5 *Motivate*: Explain how your project-specific conclusions and the general conclusions about your larger research field connect back to your research motivations. This paragraph mimics the Introduction's last paragraph. Though the Introduction's last paragraph is uncertain—i.e. it generally predicts how your project might impact your motivation—the Conclusion's last paragraph is concrete—i.e. now that you know the results, your project does impact your motivation and you can describe that impact more confidently.

Ch.11: Journal Submission Cover Letter Template

[Journal Name]
[Journal Contact Info]
[Submission Date]

Dear [Dr./Mr./Ms.] [Editor Last Name]:

Attached, please find our research article entitled **"[Title of article]"** for consideration by *[Italicized Journal Name]*.

Our study answers the research question, "[research question here]". We answer this research question by [one sentence summarizing the project—i.e. broad method, result, and conclusion, e.g. "… by using X method to produce Y result showing that Z conclusion."].

By answering this research question, our study [3 sentences connecting the project's broad motivations with the journal's mission and readership. Reword some text from your article's Introduction to connect with the journal's vision. Avoid statements like, "…our article's motivation aligns well with *Journal's* vision"—let the editor decide that. Rather, pick some key words from the journal's vision statement and work them into this paragraph.]

The literature currently overlooks this research question because [two sentences describing the research gap—i.e. weaknesses in the literature. Don't be long-winded. Don't cite specific articles. Give enough information for the editor to see that a research gap exists—i.e. your study has scientific novelty.]

We explore the research question by [one sentence describing the methods. Stay general. Focus on the important experimental features.] Our results show that [one sentence describing the main finding.] [One sentence describing the supplementary findings]. We conclude that [one sentence describing the main conclusion—i.e. the answer to the research question.] [One sentence connecting that conclusion back to the motivation and the journal's vision.]

[Another paragraph here for any additional information that the journal requires in submission cover letters—check the journal's website. This paragraph can be a bit choppy, so aim for brevity. For example, "This project was funded by XYZ funding institution. The authors have no conflicts of interest. This manuscript has not been submitted to any other journals." etc.]

We look forward to receiving comments from the selected reviewers. Please let us know if you have any questions.

Sincerely,

[Lead author name, email, and Institutional affiliation.]
[Supervisor name and Institutional affiliation.]

Ch.11: Response to Reviewers Template 1/4

[Month Day, Year]

Journal: [Name of the Journal]
Manuscript ID: [Some alphanumeric ID assigned to your manuscript]
Title: "[Title of your manuscript here]"
Author(s): [LastName1, FirstName1; LastName2, FirstName2; etc.]

Dear [Editor's Name Here],

Thank you for your comments, and we look forward to the opportunity to publish this work in [*Journal Name*]. In the next pages, we reproduce all the comments and questions provided by you and by the reviewers as well as our responses. We believe the comments from the editor and the reviewers have helped us strengthen this project and would like to thank you and the reviewers for your time and effort to help us make this an even more interesting manuscript. We have updated the manuscript to address the reviewers' questions.

Sincerely,

[Author1FirstName LastName, Author2FirstName LastName, etc.]
[Institution]
[Department]
Phone: [(###) ###-####]
Email: [leadauthoremail@institution.com]

Ch.11: Response to Reviewers Template 2/4

Response to Reviewers Document
"[Article Title]"
[LastName1, FirstName1; LastName2, FirstName2; etc.]

Comments from the Editor and Responses:

To address your comments, we have made the following changes:

(i) *Editor comment #1. Often editors will not provide their feedback as individual comments the way that reviewers do. In that case, do your best to summarize the editor's words into a series of separate comments and reproduce or summarize those comments here.*

Multiple sentences or paragraphs giving your response. This might involve responding to the editor's questions or statements as well as describing what actions you took to address those changes. If so, start with a paragraph that response to the editor's questions.

Then use a separate paragraph here to describe your actions. Be succinct but thorough. Cover all the important points, but be efficient with your grammar. At the end of this action-description paragraph, point the editor towards relevant line numbers, and then reproduce that updated portion of the manuscript by pasting it below in a smaller font, as shown in the next sentence and following quotes. Please refer to lines ###-### of the revised manuscript:

"

Verbatim text from the updated manuscript. This text comes from lines ###-### that you referred to above at the end of your action-description paragraph.

"

(ii) *Editor comment #2. Either their actual comment or the summary of the individual comment you identified from reading the editor's message.*

Your response to editor's comment here. One paragraph responding to them. One paragraph describing your actions.

"

Verbatim text from the updated manuscript. This text comes from lines ###-### that you referred to above at the end of your action-description paragraph.

"

(Repeat the above structure for each of the editor's comments.)

Ch.11: Response to Reviewers Template 3/4

Reviewer Comments and Responses:

Reviewer 1:

> *R1: "Quote Reviewer 1's opening statement here. Often this will include a summary statement of the article and some other information that you don't really need to respond to. Still, paste that information so that the entirety of the reviewer's words are quoted in this document.*
>
> *Then paste Reviewer 1's actual first comment—one that requires your response and action—here, verbatim. Once you've pasted all of their comment, end the quotation and move on to your response."*

Begin each response by thanking the reviewer for their feedback. Then jump directly into responding to their comment or answering their question. For long responses—when you're pivoting or simply providing helpful context to the reviewer—feel free to take up a paragraph with your response.

Then start a new paragraph describing your actions. Be specific. Also describe how your actions satisfy the reviewer's comment. At the end of this paragraph, point the reviewer towards relevant line numbers, and then reproduce that updated portion of the manuscript by pasting it below in a smaller font, as shown in the next sentence and following quotes. Please refer to lines ###-### of the revised manuscript:

"

Verbatim text from the updated manuscript. This text comes from lines ###-### that you referred to above at the end of your action-description paragraph. This copied text might take up a lot of space. That's okay. By putting it in a smaller text and offsetting it with quotation marks, we help it to be comprehensive without dominating the visual space of the Response to Reviewers document.

When we have long amounts of reproduced text, it won't dominate the Response to Reviewers document because the smaller text will deemphasize it and the other elements' stronger formatting will help them stand out.

"

> *R1: "Quote Reviewer 1's second comment here. Many comments will be a bit shorter and take up less visual space."*

For short responses, when simply implementing the reviewer's feedback, you can combine the response and action-description into a single paragraph. After the response, launch right into your actions. Conclude as usual: refer to the line numbers and then reproduce the text. It's okay if comments and response run from the end of one page to the beginning next. Don't feel like you need to insert strategic page breaks to keep each comment and response

Ch.11: Response to Reviewers Template 4/4

on the same page. Just keep the format consistent and the reviewers won't have any trouble keeping themselves oriented.

"

Verbatim text from the updated manuscript. Shorter comments might require smaller changes and less reproduced text.

"

> *R1: "Continue quoting the Reviewer 1's comments until you have listed and responded to all of them in the consistent format. Then move to Reviewer 2."*

For rebuttals, we don't make any changes to the revised manuscript, so we don't need to refer to any line numbers or reproduce any text. Instead, spend one paragraph thanking the reviewer for the suggestion but stating that you disagree. Then give another paragraph or two defending your position. Be gracious and succinct. You don't want any long-winded, defensive monologues here. Simply state your reasoning and provide one or two references from the literature if helpful. References can help you defend your methods, your interpretation of a result, or your conclusions. It's especially helpful to refer to a publication from the Journal that you are submitting to.

Reviewer 2:

> *R2: "Quote Reviewer 2's opening statement here. Put three empty lines—i.e. hit enter three times—when you start the comments for a new reviewer. It's important to make a strong visual signal for each reviewer to scan ahead to.*
>
> *Then paste Reviewer 2's actual first comment—one that requires your response and action—here, verbatim. Once you've pasted all of their comment, end the quotation and move on to your response."*

Some reviewer comments will be very simple. They might, for example, point out a grammatical error. In that case simply state that you corrected the error, and end as usual. Please refer to lines ###-### of the revised manuscript:

"

Verbatim text from the updated manuscript. This text comes from lines ###-###. It's short because it's just a grammar fix.

"

(Continue the above structure for the rest of the Reviewers and the rest of their comments.)

End of Response to Reviewers Document

Selected References

Though I cite additional references in the Notes section, I found the following resources particularly useful for writing this book. I hope you will find them helpful for improving your own research process and developing your particular research strengths.

Productivity

James Clear, *Atomic Habits: An Easy & Proven Way to Build Good Habits & Break Bad Ones* (Avery, 2018).

Stephen R. Covey, *The 7 Habits of Highly Effective People: Powerful Lessons in Personal Change* (DC Books, 1994).

Cal Newport, *Deep Work: Rules for Focused Success in a Distracted World* (Grand Central Publishing, 2016).

Paul J. Silvia, *How to Write a Lot: A Practical Guide to Productive Academic Writing* (APA LifeTools, 2007).

Literature Review

Christine B. Feak and John M. Swales, *Telling a Research Story: Writing a Literature Review* (University of Michigan Press, 2009).

Outlining

Jari Saramäki, *How to Write a Scientific Paper: An Academic Self-help Guide for PhD Students* (Independently Published, 2018).

Experimenting

Mildred L. Patten and Michelle Newhart *Understanding Research Methods: An Overview of the Essentials* (Routledge, 2017).

E. Bright Wilson, Jr., *An Introduction to Scientific Research* (Dover Publications, 1952).

Visualization

Scott Berinato, *Good Charts: The HBR Guide to Making Smarter, More Persuasive Data Visualizations* (Harvard Business Review Press, 2016).

Writing

Joshua Schimel, *Writing Science: How to Write Papers That Get Cited and Proposals That Get Funded* (Oxford University Press, 2011).

Editing

Roy Peter Clark, *Writing Tools: 55 Essential Strategies for Every Writer* (Little, Brown and Company, 2008).

William Strunk Jr. and E. B. White, *The Elements of Style* (Pearson, 2019).

Revision

Paul J. Silvia, *Write it Up: Practical Strategies for Writing and Publishing Journal Articles* (American Psychological Association, 2014).

Notes

Ch.1 Motivate Research with Questions

[1] Stephen R. Covey, *The 7 Habits of Highly Effective People: Powerful Lessons in Personal Change* (DC Books, 1994). Though this book includes many strategies for working more effectively, we'll focus on the concepts of "begin with the end in mind" and "interdependence."

[2] E. Bright Wilson, Jr., *An Introduction to Scientific Research* (Dover Publications, 1952). "…it is usually best to undertake experiments which are designed to test well-though-out hypotheses. Experiments for experiment's sake are much less likely to lead anywhere. The results are often not useful later because, when a new hypothesis arises, its test may require data taken under somewhat different conditions."

[3] "Frequently, a small amount of time spent restating the problem in different ways, redefining it, or expressing its limits, points the way to its solution." E. Bright Wilson, Jr., *An Introduction to Scientific Research*. See the chapter on "The choice and statement of a research problem."

[4] E. Bright Wilson, Jr., *An Introduction to Scientific Research* advises that we work in new, developing areas of our field where new breakthroughs are more likely to occur.

[5] Or, put more elegantly in E. Bright Wilson, Jr., *An Introduction to Scientific Research*, "Nature is far too vast to hope to chart its expanse in complete detail. It is therefore important that every task

undertaken should be selected because it is likely to tell us something about a wide area, rather than merely the immediate neighborhood."

Ch.2 Prioritize Deep Work

[6] National Science Foundation, *Doctorate Recipients from U.S. Universities 2018* (National Center for Science and Engineering Statistics, 2019). The median number of years from graduate school entry to earning a Science and Engineering PhD is a sobering 6-7 years. I hope the productivity framework in Part One might help you shorten that duration.

[7] Cal Newport, *Deep Work: Rules for Focused Success in a Distracted World* (Grand Central Publishing, 2016). A fascinating read that balances the philosophy of deep work and why it is a vital skill for the future with the application of deep work to your work rhythm.

[8] Cal Newport, *Digital Minimalism: Choosing a Focused Life in a Noisy World* (Portfolio, 2019). For many more ideas on applying deep work to your work rhythm, see "Part 2: The Rules" of Cal Newport, *Deep Work*. For applications specific to digital technology and digital distractions, see Cal Newport, *Digital Minimalism.*

[9] This half-hour scheduling idea comes from Cal Newport, *Deep Work*. I've tailored it here to exemplify an academic schedule.

[10] For more discussion on the balance between deep work and shallow work, see the "Drain the Shallows" chapter of Cal Newport, *Deep.*

[11] This recurring, open-door availability comes from Cal Newport, *Digital* Minimalism, which describes the concept as "holding office hours."

[12] Paul J. Silvia, *Write it Up: Practical Strategies for Writing and Publishing Journal Articles* (American Psychological Association, 2014). The idea for tracking your writing efficiency comes from this excellent book on writing productivity by Paul J. Silvia.

[13] Some people abstain from smart phones altogether by purchasing "dumb phones" with intentionally-limited features. For a robust discussion of smart phones, social media, and other digital technologies that may be stifling your productivity—not to mention your happiness—see Cal Newport, *Digital Minimalism.*

[14] Cal Newport, *Deep Work* refers to this practice of giving each workday an end as a "shutdown routine."

Ch.3 Build Consistency through Habits

[15] James Clear, *Atomic Habits: An Easy & Proven Way to Build Good Habits & Break Bad Ones* (Avery, 2018). A fascinating read on the psychology of habits and how we can apply habits to be more productive.

[16] James Clear, *James Clear and Cal Newport* (SoundCloud Podcast, October 2018, <https://soundcloud.com/jamesclear/james-clear-and-cal-newport>) An interesting podcast on the synergies between deep work and habits. "A habit is a mindless ritual that leads to deep work."

[17] Or, as described in James Clear, *Atomic Habits*: To discourage bad habits, we make cues invisible, cravings unattractive, responses difficult, and rewards unsatisfying. To reinforce good habits we make cues obvious, cravings attractive, responses easy, and rewards satisfying.

[18] For many more examples, see James Clear, *Atomic Habits.*

[19] James Clear, *James Clear and Cal Newport.*

[20] James Clear, *Atomic Habits*, "Every action you take is a vote for the type of person you wish to become."

[21] The idea of memorizing music to train your brain for deep work during your leisure time comes from Cal Newport, *Deep Work.*

[22] See Cal Newport, *Digital Minimalism* for the productivity benefits of walking and solitude.

[23] According to James Clear, *James Clear and Cal Newport* many habits are tied to a drink, in fact—primarily caffeine or alcohol. (Though you should probably avoid serving martinis in your chemistry lab.)

Ch.5 Review the Literature

[24] Christine B. Feak and John M. Swales, *Telling a Research Story: Writing a Literature Review* (University of Michigan Press, 2009). "…telling a suitable story about the relevant previous work enables you to demonstrate how your current work is situated within, builds on, or departs from earlier publications. This situating is a key aspect of [positioning your research]."

[25] Literature review is more than a listing of previous work, it estab-

lishes context for your work and highlights its potential contribution to the field. Feak and Swales, *Telling a Research Story.*

[26] "Science by its very nature is a structure which grows by the addition of new material on top of a great edifice formed by earlier workers. An individual completely ignorant of what was known before has little chance of making a worthwhile contribution." E. Bright Wilson, Jr., *An Introduction to Scientific Research.*

[27] Google Scholar (scholar.google.com) is a search engine designed for browsing the academic literature.

[28] Joshua Schimel, *Writing Science: How to Write Papers That Get Cited and Proposals That Get Funded* (Oxford University Press, 2011). I found the "IMRaD" acronym in this book.

[29] Hubbard K. E., Dunbar S. D., *Perceptions of scientific research literature and strategies for reading papers depending on academic career stage* (PLoS ONE 12(12): e0189753, 2017). Apparently, about 70% of science and engineering graduate students find the Methods section difficult to read, while only 20% of PhDs do. So don't worry—the Methods section does eventually become easier to digest.

[30] For a discussion on the balance between a thorough understanding of the literature and a familiarity with the *relevant* literature, see the "Scholars before Researchers" chapter of Feak and Swales, *Telling a Research Story.* My summary—to be a leader in your research field will require a thorough understanding of your field's literature. To finish your first journal article requires enough *relevant* research to identify a research gap, defend your methods, and compare your findings.

[31] Silvia refers to these as "Traditional Methods," and describes them as, "…staid and inoffensive, you're basically using what other people have used, so there's no controversy here, just new applications for existing methods." See Paul J. Silvia, *Write it Up.*

Ch.6 Outline the Project

[32] Jari Saramäki, *How to Write a Scientific Paper: An Academic Self-help Guide for PhD Students* (Independently Published, 2018). "…outlining helps you to be more productive. When writing without an outline, it takes a lot of time to get started, and you have to read what you have already written just to remember what you were planning to say next."

[33] "The purpose of all this outlining is to help you think more clearly. Outlining forces you to consider the big picture before spending time on details and makes it easier for you to follow your storyline." Jari Saramäki, *How to Write a Scientific Paper.*

[34] Wendy Laura Belcher, *Writing your Journal Article in Twelve Weeks* (SAGE Publications, 2009). Belcher advises that we do eventually sit down with our friends explain our project to them—their feedback and questions can be quite helpful for developing our outline. But before reaching out for feedback, do *some* preliminary work on your outline.

[35] For further discussion on summarizing the literature, see the "Constructing an Original Discussion of Previous Work" chapter of Feak and Swales, *Telling a Research Story.*

[36] "Scientific research is about observation and description. It's about data – often quantitative data. We are often studying cause and effect, trying to improve our ability to predict or control things about nature or the world. We accomplish these things by analyzing and synthesizing." E. Bright Wilson, Jr., *An Introduction to Scientific Research.*

[37] Mildred L. Patten and Michelle Newhart, *Understanding Research Methods: An Overview of the Essentials* (Routledge, 2017). This thorough book contains whole chapters about Sampling, Data, Measurements, and other subsections you might include in your Methods.

[38] Absolute versus relative accuracy, see E. Bright Wilson, Jr., *An Introduction to Scientific Research.*

[39] "A research worker in pure science who does not have at all times more problems he would like to solve than he has time and means to investigate them probably is in the wrong business." E. Bright Wilson, Jr., *An Introduction to Scientific Research.*

Ch.7 Run the Experiment

[40] Robert V. Smith, Llewellyn D. Densmore, and Edward F. Lener *Graduate Research: A Guide for Students in the Sciences* (Academic Press, 2016) provides this advice for building up your skills with an apparatus: "Recreate the results of a former lab member or study in the literature." "New studies should start with simple experiments and increase in complexity."

[41] Detailed discussion on experimental apparatus, see E. Bright Wilson, Jr., *An Introduction to Scientific Research.*

[42] "Don't trust manufacturers' or others' calibrations—be confident of the apparatus from your own calibrations." E. Bright Wilson, Jr., *An Introduction to Scientific Research.*

[43] For discussion of the null hypothesis, see E. Bright Wilson, Jr., *An Introduction to Scientific Research,* Robert V. Smith, Llewellyn D. Densmore, and Edward F. Lener *Graduate Research: A Guide for Students in the Sciences,* and Mildred L. Patten and Michelle Newhart *Understanding Research Methods.* Patten's book, in particular, provides a detailed discussion of the quantitative procedures for disproving the null hypothesis.

[44] For a discussion of various statistical tools and their applications, see Mildred L. Patten and Michelle Newhart, *Understanding Research Methods.*

[45] Effect size: a small effect in life-saving medical treatment might be wonderful, while a large effect in an experiment with no social value is not meaningful. See Mildred L. Patten and Michelle Newhart, *Understanding Research Methods.*

[46] For additional discussion on statistical significance (accuracy) and effect size (meaningfulness), see Mildred L. Patten and Michelle Newhart, *Understanding Research Methods.*

Ch.8 Visualize the Findings

[47] Scott Berinato, *Good Charts: The HBR Guide to Making Smarter, More Persuasive Data Visualizations* (Harvard Business Review Press, 2016). The idea of verbalizing the goals of a chart before trying to design it visually come from this book.

[48] Berinato describes these three chart types—comparison, distribution, composition—as the most common, but list a few others as well and provides a useful graphic for determining chart type. Scott Berinato, *Good Charts.*

[49] For more discussion on how our readers view figures, see the chapter "How we See" in Scott Berinato, *Good Charts.*

[50] Edward R. Tufte, *The Visual Display of Quantitative Information* (Graphics Press, 2001). A classic book on visualization theory. Tufte coined the terms "data ink," "chartjunk," and many others.

[51] In Tufte's perspective, pie charts have low data density—the little information given the amount of space they occupy. Many pie charts would be much better presented as tables. Edward R. Tufte, *The Visual Display of Quantitative Information*

[52] For more discussion of the pros and cons of the truncated y-axis, see the "Persuasion or Manipulation" chapter of Scott Berinato, *Good Charts.*

[53] For more discussion of the pros and cons of the double y-axis, see the "Persuasion or Manipulation" chapter of Scott Berinato, *Good Charts.*

[54] Tufte refers to this method of stacking multiple charts with the same x-axis as "small multiples." Edward R. Tufte, *The Visual Display of Quantitative Information.*

[55] In other words, the x-axis shows the cause, and the y-axis shows the effect. Edward R. Tufte, *The Visual Display of Quantitative Information.*

[56] These questions derived from the "Visual Crit" chapter of Scott Berinato, *Good Charts.*

Ch.9 Write the First Draft

[57] Anne Lamott, *Bird by Bird: Some Instructions on Writing and Life* (Random House, 2014). Lamott terms the phrase "shitty first drafts" in this book along with the advice: "Most of your drafts are just going to be bad. In your first drafts, just try to get the words out."

[58] Along with great writing advice, Saramäki provides useful advice for selecting a journal to submit your work to. Jari Saramäki, *How to Write a Scientific Paper*

[59] If you want to learn a lot more about scientific writing, I highly recommend Joshua Schimel, *Writing Science.* It is well-written, deep, and contains many examples and illustrations.

[60] For additional storytelling concepts, see the chapter on "What Makes a Good Story" in Joshua Schimel, *Writing Science.*

[61] Paul J. Silvia, *How to Write a Lot: A Practical Guide to Productive Academic Writing* (APA LifeTools, 2007). Writing a bit every day boosts your writing productivity. See also Anne Lamott, *Bird by Bird.*

[62] For more on the pitfalls of binge writing, see the "Specious Barriers to Writing a Lot" chapter in Paul J. Silvia, *How to Write a Lot.*

[63] Robert Boice, *Professors as Writers* (New Forums Press, 1990). People who write daily are not only more productive, but also generate more creative ideas (compared to those who write when they feel like it).

[64] Paragraphs are the main component of writing. See Joshua Schimel, *Writing Science.*

[65] "The paragraph-level outline should, at the very least, contain the topics of each paragraph and the points those paragraphs should make. It can also include notes, bulleted lists, sketches of arguments, and the points that those paragraphs should make." Jari Saramäki, *How to Write a Scientific Paper.*

[66] For additional ideas on how to critique the literature, see the "Taking a Stance Toward the Literature" chapter of Feak and Swales, *Telling a Research Story.*

[67] "We only study parts of nature—not the whole thing. And we hope that our knowledge of that part of nature can be synthesized with other knowledge to reveal new knowledge about nature as a whole." E. Bright Wilson, Jr., *An Introduction to Scientific Research.*

[68] The first section of an article, and the first paragraph of a section are important for hooking the reader—they should raise questions that go unanswered for now, which piques the readers curiosity. See Jari Saramäki, *How to Write a Scientific Paper.*

[69] For more on the goals of the Methods section and how those goals influence the way we write it, see Joshua Schimel, *Writing Science.*

[70] Reviewers will always find something to critique about your article. An article with a few minor flaws gives the reviewers something to comment on. Wendy Laura Belcher, *Writing your Journal Article in Twelve Weeks.*

[71] Roy Peter Clark, *Writing Tools: 55 Essential Strategies for Every Writer* (Little, Brown and Company, 2008). "Cut the big limbs first, then shake out the leaves." I.e., edit the larger elements first and work your way down to the smaller elements. (There is no use trimming leaves if the whole limb needs pruning.)

[72] The concept of "point-first" and "point-last" paragraph types comes from Joshua Schimel, *Writing Science.*

[73] For a detailed discussion of active verses passive voice, see Joshua Schimel, *Writing Science.*

Ch.10 Edit the Second Draft

[74] Express your best thought in your shortest sentence. A short sentence gains power from proximity to a longer sentence. See Roy Peter Clark, *Writing Tools.*

[75] William Strunk Jr. and E. B. White, *The Elements of Style* (Pearson, 2019). A classic, succinct book containing many prescriptive edits with examples. The word-editing list in this book draws heavily from *Elements of Style* as well as Roy Peter Clark, *Writing Tools*, and Wendy Laura Belcher, *Writing your Journal Article in Twelve Weeks*.

[76] Focus on strong verbs and accurate nouns, see Strunk and White, *The Elements of Style.*

[77] Nominalizations emasculate verbs, see Joshua Schimel, *Writing Science.*

[78] Editing adverbs, see Roy Peter Clark, *Writing Tools.*

[79] Remove verb qualifiers, see Roy Peter Clark, *Writing Tools.*

[80] Editing the word, "while," see Strunk and White, *The Elements of Style.*

[81] Editing the word, "effect," see Strunk and White, *The Elements of Style.*

[82] Clusters of prepositions often signal unneeded phrases and wordy sentences, see Wendy Laura Belcher, *Writing your Journal Article in Twelve Weeks.*

[83] Karen Kelsky, *The Professor is In* (Three Rivers Press, 2015). Dyads have a particularly numbing affect because they can feel too rhythmic and sing-songy when placed one after another. A few dyads and lists is okay, but a reliance on them makes for sleepy reading.

[84] If you're thirsty for even more editing, you can find an epic editing checklist in Wendy Laura Belcher, *Writing your Journal Article in Twelve Weeks.*

[85] Velany Rodrigues, *How to write an effective title and abstract and choose appropriate keywords* (editage Insights, 2013, < www.editage.com/insights/how-to-write-an-effective-title-and-abstract-and-choose-appropriate-keywords>). The idea for testing your keywords by putting them into a search engine comes from here.

[86] I adopted Rodrigues' idea of starting with a long title and trimming it down. See Velany Rodrigues, *How to write an effective title and abstract and choose appropriate keywords.*

[87] Luz Claudio, *How to Write and Publish a Scientific Paper* (Independently Published, 2016). I adopted Claudio's idea on building the abstract by compiling your article's best sentences and reworking them.

Ch.11 Revise until Published

[88] Tackle the revision process with a constructive attitude. Believe that the peer-review process makes most papers better. See the "Dealing with Journals" chapter of Paul J. Silvia, *Write it Up.*

[89] Jari Saramäki, *How to Write a Scientific Paper* describes this idea as "extreme editing" and provides many tips for how to sit down with your supervisor (or other colleagues) to edit an article together.

[90] Or, if your supervisor continues to avoid you, consider more extreme measures from Paul J. Silvia—a professor and research supervisor himself: "Try to get someone else to push your advisor around. Why not complain to another faculty member, the department chair, or the director of graduate studies? If that doesn't work, photocopy this section of the book and anonymously leave it in your advisor's mailbox. The brash can attach it to a copy of their manuscript. Finally, set a deadline for your advisor and submit the paper yourself. The unwillingness to read a student's paper and provide scomments shows a lack of commitment to graduate training and the process of science. Say, 'I really need to submit this within 4 weeks,' and remind the person 2 weeks and 3 weeks later." Paul J. Silvia, *How to Write a Lot.*

[91] "Set deadlines for your co-authors. Submit the paper when the deadline passes. A friend of mine sent a derelict coauthor an email with 'You're off the paper' as the subject. That worked." Paul J. Silvia, *How to Write a Lot.*

[92] For more tips on getting good editing feedback from your colleagues, see the "Giving, Getting, and Using Others' Feedback" chapter of Wendy Laura Belcher, *Writing your Journal Article in Twelve Weeks.*

[93] For more on the back-and-forth experienced during the internal revision process, see Joshua Schimel, *Writing Science.*

[94] "You'll write better when you expect rejection, because you'll mute the need to avoid failure. Writers motivated by failure avoidance write papers that sound defensive, wishy-washy, and uncertain. Instead of trying to look good, they try not to look bad. Readers can feel the fear. Writers motivated by the need to achieve success, in contrast, write papers that sound confident and controlled. These writers focus on the strengths of the work, assert

the importance of the research, and convey a persuasive sense of confidence." Paul J. Silvia, *How to Write a Lot.*

[95] For more on the same reviewers participating in the peer-review process for your backup journal, see Paul J. Silvia, *Write it Up.*

[96] "If the editor encourages you to submit a revised version, do it—she is already on your side. If the editor uses less encouraging words like 'should you wish to resubmit a revised version', do it anyway because even in this case the door is still open." Jari Saramäki, *How to Write a Scientific Paper.*

[97] "A few [reviewer comments] are weird, incomprehensible, self-serving, or just ask too much without benefitting the article. Editors don't expect you to make every change. If you resist, give good reasons." Paul J. Silvia, *Write it Up.*

[98] In Silvia's words, you can "change, resist, or punt." See Paul J. Silvia, *Write it Up.*

[99] You should change your manuscript to accommodate most of the reviewers' comments. See Paul J. Silvia, *Write it Up.*

[100] For more on developing your revision to-do list, see Paul J. Silvia, *Write it Up.*

[101] The Response to Reviewers document is at least as important—if not more important—than the actual revised manuscript. The editor and reviewers will read this document more closely than they will read the revised article. Paul J. Silvia, *Write it Up.*

Epilogue: What Next?

[102] The combined effect of multiple publications in the same research field, see the "One of Many: Building a Body of Work" chapter of Paul J. Silvia, *Write it Up.*

Made in the USA
Monee, IL
22 July 2022